Moral and Ethical Implications of
HUMAN ORGAN TRANSPLANTS

MORE THINE THAN MINE

Three score and ten
Doled to most men —
But with countless
Surprised organs implanted in me
Will I be I
Or some stranger, at ten score and three

— *The Pharos, July 1969*
(Used by permission.)

Moral and Ethical Implications of
HUMAN ORGAN TRANSPLANTS

By

GEORGE W. MILLER, A.B., B.D., Th.M., Th.D.

Senior Chaplain
Director of Pastoral Care
Baptist Hospital of Miami, Inc.
Miami, Florida
Fellow, College of Chaplains
Past President, Southern Baptist Association of Hospital Chaplains
Founding Member, Association of Clinical Pastoral Educators

With a Foreword by

Dwight E. Harken, M.D.

Clinical Professor of Surgery
Harvard Medical School
Chief, Thoracic Surgery Department
Peter Bent Brigham Hospital
Boston, Massachusetts

CHARLES C THOMAS • PUBLISHER
Springfield • Illinois • U.S.A.

Published and Distributed Throughout the World by
CHARLES C THOMAS • PUBLISHER
Bannerstone House
301-327 East Lawrence Avenue, Springfield, Illinois, U.S.A.
Natchez Plantation House
735 North Atlantic Boulevard, Fort Lauderdale, Florida, U.S.A.

*With THOMAS BOOKS careful attention is given to all details of
manufacturing and design. It is the Publisher's desire to present books that are
satisfactory as to their physical qualities and artistic possibilities and
appropriate for their particular use. THOMAS BOOKS will be true to those
laws of quality that assure a good name and good will.*

Printed in the United States of America
RNN-1

To
SARAH, JAMIE and STEPHEN

FOREWORD

Therefore our politic Asklepios may be supposed to have exhibited the power of his Art only to persons who, being of a generally healthy constitution and habit of life, have a definite ailment. Such as these he cures by purges and operations and bids them live as usual, herein consulting the interests of the State. But bodies that disease has penetrated through and through, he will not have attempted to cure by gradual processes of evacuation or infusion. He does not want to lengthen out good-for-nothing lives or to have weak fathers begetting weaker sons. If a man is not able to live in the ordinary way, he has no business to cure him, for such a cure would be of no use, either to himself or to the State.

Plato's Republic, 400 B.C.

. . . too cruel and fascistic for Democracy in Christian 1971 . . . but still has considerable historical perspective.

Knowledgeable men of diverse disciplines share common moral bases, if, they be also men of conscience, empathy and integrity.

Men of Medicine have been wounded recently by the naive and superficial platitude, *"Heart transplants have made doctors play God!"* Such ignorance overlooks centuries of physician burdens, implies frivolous stewardship of those responsibilities and compounds both by blasphemous identification.

Physicians have predicated these life and death decisions on precarious premises. Hopefully these premises are becoming firmer but are still far from absolute. The pain of doubt and poor alternatives exclude the mockery of "playing." Involvement of the Deity, yes, but rather as it represents the physician's prayer for helpful consultation from any honorable source.

These life and death judgments embrace imponderables. What is optimum therapy? How precise is the prognosis? How does one evaluate life in breadth as well as length? To compound these with too little medical care in both quality and quantity is to humble the decision makers.

The Reverend Doctor Miller is to be thanked for his sophisticated explorations that may afford better public insight. Through Reverend Miller, laymen may discover that the decision making is neither new nor welcome. Perhaps this sort of communication will press physicians to reach harder toward absolutes of quality, the public toward enlightened tolerance and men of the Church and Court to smooth the bridges between.

DWIGHT EMARY HARKEN, M.D.

PREFACE

O N Thursday evening, May 19, 1966, I had the distinct privilege of serving on a panel with several distinguished members of the medical profession. The occasion was the sixteenth annual Post Graduate Seminar, sponsored by the Mount Sinai Hospital of Miami Beach, Florida, and under the chairmanship of Doctor Solomon D. Goldman. The topic of our panel discussion was "Far Advanced Cancer." The physicians spoke within their disciplines about the medical and surgical risks and results with cancer patients. There was discussion about the terminal patient and the limitations of the medical profession in seeking to effect certain cures, or to sustain life under the shadow of far advanced cancer. My role called for the discussion of the spiritual and emotional needs of the far advanced cancer patient and his family.

When each of the panel members had presented his paper, the moderator of the panel, Ivor Fix, M.D., opened the floor for questions and discussion. A question was put to me by a young intern: "Suppose you were called in for counsel and this case was presented: 'A patient is in the Intensive Care Unit of your hospital. She is a victim of an automobile accident, and has been injured critically. She is on the machine and is being kept *alive* by artificial means. There is another patient whose kidneys are diseased beyond treatment. The patient will die if a kidney transplant cannot be performed shortly. The patient on the machine has two good kidneys, but without the machine, she is dead.' What, chaplain, would you advise?"

The auditorium was whisper-quiet. I said, "I would advise the physician to cut off the machine, take the victim's good kidneys and give them to the patient who has a chance at life." The young physicians stood and applauded my remarks.

Later, at home that same evening, I began to think about this problem. Had I answered correctly? Was the answer, so quick to come, morally right? Had I answered responsibly and with proper concern for and empathy with all members of the families affected by so great a decision? Is it right to take vital organs from one patient and give them to another? Was this an infringement upon God's right to determine who lives and who dies? Can one morally will to spare another's life with the giving up of his own? Who should make the decision to turn off the machine? Who should actually press the "off" button? Is the one who makes the decision a murderer, or is the one who presses the button guilty? Are either guilty? How long must one utilize the use of artificial means to stimulate life? What is life? What is death? When does life begin? When is one really dead? Can one who could live with a transplanted organ be denied his chance because someone or everyone lacks the courage to turn off a switch? Was the patient on the machine already dead? What are the criteria for determining death?

These questions continually came into my mind that night, and after the applause of the young physicians had long since died down, I wondered if my answer was theologically and morally correct?

It was that night that the decision was made that I would give myself to the task of exploring the entire problem and seeking answers that would satisfy my mind.

I did not know then that, within a very short time, these questions I faced would be faced many times by physicians, attorneys, clergymen, hospital administrators and others — for their answers would be inseparably bound up with thoughts and feelings concerning the transplanting of hearts, lungs, livers and other such vital organs necessary to sustain life.

When the door was opened that I may complete the requirements for the doctor of theology degree, I immediately chose as the subject of my dissertation the title: "A Critical Analysis of the Moral and Ethical Implications of Human Organ Transplants." If I was concerned with these questions and issues, were not others within the clergy and in medicine? Were not countless multitudes in the other professions such as attorneys, teachers and professors faced with these questions? Were not the people at large concerned, since they or some of their loved ones could possibly be a recipient or donor? I decided that this was a new field in which little had been written and about which there seemed to be more interest and less knowledge, more questions and fewer answers.

I sought for and gained approval from Doctor Robert Witty, President of Luther Rice Seminary and my major professor and advisor. He offered me every encouragement, and for his guidance I shall remain grateful. I then turned to my administrator and friend, Ernest C. Nott, Jr., who both encouraged me to pursue this study and maintained an understanding attitude during the long and tedious period of study that followed. My many friends and respected colleagues in the medical profession offered their support and counsel. My friends and peers in the ministry and in the specialized area of the hospital chaplaincy were kind and helpful to me, offering cooperation exceeding that for which I had called. In correspondence with members of the legal profession and in communication with practicing physicians all over the United States and in many foreign countries, I always found a warm reception, mutual interest in and an offer to help me in my research. Hospital administrators, professors of ethics and theology, pastors, priests and rabbis — many of whom I have never met — have been of unlimited value to me, and for their help I am most grateful.

The encouragement offered me by Doctor Donald Manuel, friend and co-laborer in Miami, has been greatly appreciated. My own associate in the Department of Religion and Pastoral Care at Baptist Hospital of Miami, Inc., Chaplain T. Luther Jones, has offered help in the most tangible manner — he has assumed a good work load and spared me time to do this research. The medical social worker, Miss Sandra Bell; the foreign language intrepreter, Doctor Jose de Amezola, and my secretaries, Mrs. Lee C. Fisher and Mrs. Marjorie Hahn, have all been kind enough to understand the pressures of this research, thus making my task as their supervisor less exacting. The librarian at Baptist Hospital, Mrs. Dorothy Hindman, has helped to locate material for me and I owe her my sincere appreciation.

A special word of thanks is due my family for their cooperation, love and understanding. Sarah, my lovely wife, has been very understanding during my long period of study and research. Jamie, our daughter, has used some of her vacation time between semesters in college to help compile results from questionnaires, and I appreciate her help. Stephen, our son, has been more concerned about my research than he would openly admit, and he has used many hours during my absence to prove his genuine concern by being an exceptionally good boy.

In the quest of learning, one owes so much to so many, and each understands that acknowledgment cannot be adequately made for all the help one receives along the way. But if this work serves to offer some light on a very difficult subject, then all the help, whether formally acknowledged or not, will have been shown in the deep gratitude of this writer.

GEORGE W. MILLER

INTRODUCTION

THIS book is entitled MORAL AND ETHICAL IMPLICATIONS OF HUMAN ORGAN TRANSPLANTS. It can hardly be called an exhaustive study, because of the rapid strides being made in the field of organ transplantation. Recommendations and conclusions reached today may be sadly obsolete tomorrow, owing to the successes or failures of this rapidly changing age. Still, it offers an honest look into the accomplishments of the immediate past and the present. It is a study of the successes and failures encountered thus far. It is an attempt to examine the issues seen and unseen, felt and experienced both actually and vicariously, and is an effort to offer some reasonable and practical recommendations and to draw some conclusions on this very weighty subject.

STATEMENT OF THE PROBLEM

This book is not an attempt to prove or disprove whether or not there are moral and ethical implications involved in the transplantation of human organs. This study begins on the assumption that there *are* moral and ethical implications involved and seeks to delve into these implications to determine their extent and to ascertain how they can help or hinder in the development of this method of treating disease and sustaining life. It will seek to determine the depth of moral and ethical concerns, and will also seek to differentiate between real moral and ethical implications and those which are implied.

This research poses no threat of policing, standing in judgment, or of rendering a verdict toward any group. It lays no claim of absolute or final authority. It allows for other, more advanced study in the field and will applaud the efforts of and welcome the interest from others who will surely work on this question. It will seek to shed light on this phase of our research from the study of the Bible, from the study of humanity, and from the study of the donor and recipient respectively.

What this research cannot do, because of its confinement as to time and place, is to measure individually and personally each person who has been directly involved either as a donor or as a recipient and to have their answers recorded. It can offer that which by direct quotation or that which is reputed to have been stated verbally or in writing, as to what the donor or his family may have felt, and that which the recipient or his family may have shared in their respective involvement in the transplantation of vital human organs.

METHOD OF RESEARCH

In order to sample the thinking of others, six different questionnaires were drawn up and mailed to the following: (1) each of the fifty attorneys general in the United States; (2) one hundred chaplains of all different denominational backgrounds who serve in hospitals in the United States and in some foreign countries; (3) one hundred administrators of hospitals of varying size, including private, denominational and governmental; (4) three hundred practicing physicians, including varieties of specialists from a cross-section of the United States and foreign countries; (5) one hundred ministers, priests, and rabbis representing the parish clergy of the three major faiths plus several denominational backgrounds; (6) one hundred professors teaching ethics, psychology, and theology in colleges, universities and seminaries across the land. In all, a total of 750 questionnaires were mailed with an enclosed self-addressed stamped envelope for their replies. A total of 337 questionnaires were received, giving an overall return of 45 percent. The percentage breakdown for each category is as follows:

Mailed to	Number	Returned	Percentage
Attorneys general	50	34	70%
Hospital chaplains	100	48	48%

Hospital administrators	100	62	62%
Physicians	300	88	29%
Pastors, priests and rabbis	100	61	61%
Professors in colleges, universities and seminaries	100	44	44%

These questionnaires were designed to gain objective opinions and since no one was required to sign his name, there was afforded to each the freedom of anonymity. These questionnaires were carefully compiled and the results noted. Many of those in each category showed their keen interest and mutual concern by taking the extra time in sending multiple paged comments both in typed and handwritten form.

The difficulty of gathering data by use of questionnaires is in the phrasing of the questions. It is extremely difficult to communicate to those to whom questionnaires are sent just what data is requested and still keep the questions short. Allowance must be made for an answer to be brief, and yet be adequate. Again, a questionnaire has worth only as the researcher can tabulate and interpret his findings. It is desired that after sufficient number of returns have been processed, trends will emerge that will help to establish certain facts to support the theories and hypotheses that have before been advanced. The results of these questionnaires seem to have produced data that supports certain hypotheses and leads to some conclusions.

HYPOTHESIS: THERE ARE MORAL AND ETHICAL IMPLICATIONS INVOLVED IN TRANSPLANTATION OF HUMAN ORGANS, AND HOSPITAL CHAPLAINS ARE DIVIDED IN THEIR FEELINGS ABOUT THEM.

When one hundred hospital chaplains were asked the question — "Do you have any reservations about the moral or ethical implications of transplantation?" — of the forty-six who answered this question, fifteen responded in the affirmative, and thirty-one replied in the negative. But when they were asked if their particular denomination had an official policy as to the morality of human organ transplantation, of the forty-seven who answered this question, only four stated "Yes," while forty-three replied

"No." Of the four who had answered "Yes," two stated they had stronger standards established if the organ involved was the heart.

When asked if they felt hospital chaplains had a professional responsibility in the area of organ transplantation, of the forty-nine who answered this question, forty-seven replied "Yes" and only two answered "No."

When asked if they had been personally involved in dialogue with persons concerned with human organ transplantation, of the forty-eight who answered this question, twenty-nine replied "Yes" and nineteen said "No." Of these twenty-nine, eleven said they had talked with patients and their families while eighteen said they had talked with physicians.

When asked if they felt that transplantation of the human heart posed any moral or ethical problems not found in any other organ transplants, of the forty-six who answered this question, thirteen replied "Yes" and thirty-three said "No."

When asked if they had ever counseled a donor or recipient concerning the theological or ethical issues involved, of the forty-seven who answered this question, thirteen said they had counseled the donor, six had counseled the recipient, while twenty-eight admitted not having counseled either.

When asked if they had ever given a lecture or sermon either in support of, or in opposition to, human organ transplantation, of the forty-eight who answered this question, two had spoken in support of organ transplants, one had spoken in opposition to it, while forty-five had not discussed the matter at all.

When asked if they felt a person has a right to die in dignity, all of the forty-five who answered this question replied "Yes." A companion question asked if they believed it was wrong to sustain life by artificial means, and of the forty-three who answered this question, eight stated "Yes," twelve said "No," and twenty-three replied that their answer must be qualified. In the main, they stated that one should not be sustained as a human vegetable.

It was pointed out that with the transplantation of the human heart, many hospitals and physicians have reconsidered what constitutes death, and that definitions of death had come under closer scrutiny. The hospital chaplains were asked, "In light of this, do you feel any adjustments in your theology concerning the soul are needed?" Of the forty-four who answered this question, sixteen said "Yes," twenty-two said "No," and six said "Maybe." Some added additional phrases such as, "I don't deal in souls, I deal in persons," or "I don't know what you mean by, 'soul.' " Some refused to commit themselves and defended by stating that the question was ridiculous.

One may draw these conclusions regarding the feelings of the hospital chaplains:

1. Thirty-one have no reservations about the moral or ethical implications of transplantation of human organs, while fifteen do have reservations.
2. Forty-seven stated that hospital chaplains do have professional responsibility in the area, while only two feel that they have no responsibility.
3. Forty-five stated they had not voiced opposition to transplant proceedings, while one had opposed and two had voiced support in either sermons or lectures.
4. Chaplains were unanimous in their answers that persons have a right to die in dignity, but they were divided in whether or not artificial means should be used to sustain life. The vote: eight stated it was wrong to use artificial means, twelve stated it was not wrong, and twenty-three desired to qualify their answers.
5. Chaplains feel, in the main, that no theological adjustments are needed in view of newer definitions of death. Only sixteen agreed that adjustments were needed, twenty-two opposed the need, and six disliked the use of the word "soul."
6. The most obvious conclusion is that in view of their close association with physicians and patients who may be involved in vital organ transplantation, improvement could be made in their approach to the matter, either in more support of or in opposition to, should they so feel.

HYPOTHESIS: THERE ARE MORAL AND ETHICAL IMPLICATIONS INVOLVED IN TRANSPLANTATION OF HUMAN ORGANS, AND PHYSICIANS WELCOME THE AID OF THE CLERGY.

Three hundred questionnaires were sent to practicing physicians in various parts of the United States and in foreign countries. When they were asked the question — "Do you feel there is a problem of morality or ethics involved in major human organ transplantation?" — of the seventy who answered the question, forty stated "Yes," while thirty answered "No." When asked if they believed clergy could be of assistance to the medical profession in the area of organ transplantation, the results were three to one in the affirmative. On this basis, one may conclude the following:

1. Physicians recognize moral and ethical problems exist in the area of organ transplantation.
2. Physicians welcome the counsel from the members of the clergy and list various ways in which this help could come, such as the following:
   1) Offer support for the families of the donor and the recipient.
   2) Serve in reeducation of the public.
   3) Help to define life and death.
   4) Encourage the donation of bodies to medical science for research.
   5) Counsel physicians.

HYPOTHESIS: THERE ARE MORAL AND ETHICAL IMPLICATIONS INVOLVED IN HUMAN ORGAN TRANSPLANTATION, AND PROFESSORS IN COLLEGES, UNIVERSITIES AND SEMINARIES ARE NOT IN AGREEMENT THAT GOOD JUDGMENT AND THOROUGH RESEARCH HAS ESTABLISHED TRANSPLANTATION PROCEDURE. THEY DID AGREE IT WILL BE WIDELY USED IN THE FUTURE.

One hundred questionnaires were sent to the professors of ethics and theology in colleges, universities and seminaries. When these professors were asked the question — "Do you believe there are any ethical or moral problems in major human organ transplantation?" — of the thirty-nine who answered this question, thirty replied "Yes," while only nine answered in the negative. But when asked if they personally had any theological or moral reservations regarding major human organ transplantation, of the forty-one who answered the question, only five replied, "Yes," while thirty-six stated "No," and further qualified their negative replies by two stating opposition to heart transplants and three opposing any attempt to transplant the brain.

When asked the question — "Have any of you written or lectured on the subject of morality of human organ transplantation?" — of the forty-two who answered the question, eleven replied "Yes" and thirty-one replied "No."

When asked the question — "Do you believe that good judgment and thorough research has backed each heart transplant?" — of the thirty-seven who answered, fifteen replied "Yes," seven stated "No," thirteen answered, "Don't know," while two stated their answer must be qualified.

When asked the question — "Do you basically agree that major organ transplantation has arrived and will be widely used in the future?" — of the thirty-nine who answered, thirty-seven replied "Yes," one answered "No," and one stated "Probably."

One may then conclude:

1. Professors recognize moral and ethical implications involving human organ transplants.
2. They had personal reservations about the morality and ethics involved.
3. Of the professionals, excluding physicians, professors have outdistanced others in writing and lecturing in this area.
4. Professors were divided in their decisions concerning the adequacy of research and use of good judgment prior to heart transplantation procedures.
5. The professors were near-unanimous in their feeling that major human organ transplantation has arrived and will be widely used in the future. The vote: thirty-seven answered "Yes," one "No," and one "Probably."

HYPOTHESIS: THERE ARE MORAL AND ETHICAL IMPLICATIONS INVOLVING HUMAN ORGAN TRANSPLANTATION, AND PARISH CLERGYMEN OF THE THREE MAJOR FAITHS AND A VARIETY OF DENOMINATIONAL BACKGROUNDS FEEL THEY HAVE A PROFESSIONAL RESPONSIBILITY IN THE AREA, BUT THAT NO CHANGES IN THEOLOGY REGARDING THE SOUL IS NECESSARY.

One hundred questionnaires were sent to parish clergymen (ministers, priests and rabbis). When they were quizzed as to whether it was morally wrong to transplant human organs, of the fifty-seven who answered this question, only three answered "Yes," while fifty-four replied "No."

When asked if there were reservations as to the type of human organ transplants, of the sixty who answered this question, ten replied "Yes" and fifty answered "No." Of the ten who had replied "Yes," five of these stated objections to attempts to transplant the brain and five stated opposition to the transplanting of the heart.

When asked if a sermon had been preached either in support of, or in opposition to, organ transplantation, of the sixty who answered this question, fifty-six reported they had not preached in support of organ transplantation while only four admitted they had preached in support of it; fifty-seven replied that they had not preached in opposition to human organ transplantation while three stated they had preached in opposition to it.

When asked if they had personally been involved in dialogue with persons concerned with human organ transplantation, of the fifty-seven who answered this question, thirty said "Yes" and twenty-seven replied "No." Of those who had answered in the affirmative, six had held dialogue with patients, ten with members of the family, eight with physicians, and ten with others — including friends, nurses, other pastors, parishionners, on panels, and in general study groups.

When asked if they had been consulted by a donor or a recipient concerning theological, ethical or moral issues involved, of the fifty-nine who answered the former (donor), six replied "Yes" and fifty-three stated "No." In the latter (recipient), of the forty-eight who answered, two replied "Yes" and forty-six replied "No."

When asked if their particular denomination had an official policy as to the morality of human organ transplantation, of the fifty-eight who answered this question, only seven replied "Yes," while fifty-one stated "No." Of those who answered "Yes" (when asked if it offered stronger standards of morality if the organ involved is the heart), of these seven, three said "Yes" and four said "No."

When asked if pastors had any professional responsibilities in the area of human organ transplantation, of the fifty-four who answered this question, thirty-eight replied "Yes" and sixteen stated "No." Of those who replied "Yes," it was asked if they felt physicians would welcome their counsel and of these thirty-eight, twenty-five said "Yes," nine said "No," and four stated "Maybe."

When asked the question — "In light of the transplant age and the changing definition of the time of death, do you feel theology has any adjustments or changes to make regarding the soul?" — of the fifty-four who answered, seven replied "Yes," and forty-seven replied "No."

One may conclude:

1. Ministers, priests and rabbis in the parish feel fifty-four to three that it is not morally wrong to transplant human organs, but reservations were expressed regarding the transplanting of the heart by five, and of attempts to transplant the brain, there were five opposing.
2. These parish clergymen, representing the three major faiths, have failed to give voice either for or against the transplanting of human organs.
3. Parish clergy are called upon to communicate with persons involved in organ transplantation. Ten have talked with members of the family, eight with physicians, and ten with others — including each other.
4. Denominational policies regarding transplanting of organs are almost nonexistent. Only seven denominations stated such a policy, while 51 denied having any.
5. Although parish clergymen feel they have definite professional responsibilities in the field of transplants, thirty-eight to sixteen, and believe that physicians would welcome their counsel, they have remained strangely silent.
6. Although physicians are redefining death and the time at which life passes away, parish clergymen voted forty-seven to seven that there are no needed theological adjustments to be made.

HYPOTHESIS: THERE ARE LEGAL IMPLICATIONS INVOLVED IN
HUMAN ORGAN TRANSPLANTATION, AND

ATTORNEYS GENERAL ARE INVOLVED IN
LEGISLATIVE PROCEDURES POINTING TOWARD
CERTAIN LEGAL REQUIREMENTS.

A questionnaire was sent to each attorney general in the fifty states. To the question as to whether their state had any statute regarding the transplantation of major human organs, of the thirty-four who answered this question, eleven said "Yes," eleven said "No," and twelve indicated that legislation was pending.

Of twenty-two who were asked whether they had been called upon to issue an opinion as to the moral, ethical or legal aspects of human organ transplantation, all said "No."

Asked whether there were any statutes that specified the physician's responsibility in the use of artificial means in sustaining life, of the twenty who replied, all said "No."

When asked if, in the event of major human organ transplantation taking place in his state, there would be definite legal requirements, of the thirty-four who responded to this question, eighteen replied "Yes" and sixteen answered "No." These legal requirements involve determination of clinical death, the granting of permission for removal of organs to be transplanted, and the willing of one's body to medical schools or research centers for use after death.

When asked if there were any known suits against physicians or hospitals involving organ transplantation, the answer of those responding was unanimous, with all twenty-three replying in the negative.

One may conclude:

1. While all states have not passed into law definite statutes regarding legal implications involved in human organ transplantation, many have and more are.
2. Use of artificial means to sustain life is not a legal requirement of physicians, but there are legal requirements to determine clinical death if organs are to be transplanted.
3. The Uniform Anatomical Gift Act, resulting from legislative work in the area of human organ transplantation, is being adopted by virtually all fifty states.
4. The Uniform Anatomical Gift Act, to be discussed at length later, will set the legal scale on which any proposed suit in

the area of organ transplantation shall be weighed.
HYPOTHESIS: MAJOR ORGAN TRANSPLANTATION SHOULD BE
CONFINED TO THOSE CERTAIN HOSPITALS AND/OR
MEDICAL CENTERS WHICH ARE DESIGNED AND
EQUIPPED TO BEAR THIS RESPONSIBILITY AND
HOSPITAL ADMINISTRATORS CONCUR.

One hundred questionnaires were sent to administrators of hospitals and medical centers throughout the country. When asked the question — "How many beds does your institution contain?" — of the fifty-eight who answered this question, one had less than 100; sixteen had from 100 to 200; fourteen had from 200 to 300; six had from 300 to 400; thirteen had from 400 to 500; four had from 500 to 600; one had from 600 to 700; zero had from 700 to 800, 800 to 900, or 900 to 1,000; and three had from 1,000 to 1,500.

When asked to state whether their hospitals had either an intensive care unit or intensive coronary care unit, both, an intensive care unit only, or an intensive coronary care unit only, of the sixty-one who answered, three had neither, thirty-six had both, seventeen had an intensive care unit only, and five had an intensive coronary care unit only.

To the question — "Have any human organ transplants been done in your hospital?" — of the sixty-two who answered, nine replied "Yes" and fifty-three said "No."

When asked whether any patients were then awaiting a possible transplant in their institution, of the fifty-one who answered, three replied "Yes" and forty-eight said "No."

When asked if there had been any official action by the Board of Trustees and/or the medical staff regarding the transplantation of human organs, of the fifty-nine who answered, two replied "Yes" and fifty-seven said "No."

One may conclude:

1. The large majority of hospitals in America range in size from 100 to 500 beds.
2. The majority of hospitals, whatever their bed capacity, have both intensive care units, as well as intensive coronary care units.
3. The majority of hospitals in the country have not had major

organ transplants performed therein.

4. The majority of hospitals in the country do not have patients awaiting a possible transplant of vital human organs.

5. The majority of hospitals quizzed stated that no official action had been taken regarding human organ transplants.

6. The majority of hospitals do not plan for, nor contemplate the transplanting of, major human organs in their institutions. It seems reasonable and just that only certain hospitals and/or medical centers specially prepared and equipped should or will offer major organ transplantation as a part of their patient care.

7. It would seem that it would be morally wrong for a hospital to engage in the transplantation of vital human organs when not equipped by proper space, personnel, facilities, financial backing or established rules of procedure.

8. It would seem that it would be morally wrong when so equipped as to proper space, personnel, facilities, financial backing and established rules of procedure not to offer the research, including transplantation of vital human organs, that may alleviate human suffering and/or sustain meaningful life.

"For unto whomsoever much is given, of him shall much be required: and to whom men have committed much, of him they will ask the more." (Luke 12:48)

THE LITERATURE

The subject of this study is not one upon which much has been written. It is not one which affords the writer the luxury of a library of books and other bound volumes to which ready reference may be made. Indeed, the literature is largely limited to material found in journals, magazines and newspapers. The primary source of this research, then, is found in the questionnaire discussed earlier, the reference to the limited number of books upon the overall subject of transplantation of organs, and the material written in journals, magazines and newspapers on current organ transplants.

The unique position of the writer, who serves as chaplain of a hospital, has afforded him access to the medical library and to the latest journals which record the progress, successes and failures of organ transplantation. In addition, another primary source was the subscribing to a clipping service which has a monthly reading span of some 15,000 to 20,000 journals, newspapers and periodicals. These readers clipped and mailed to the writer any and all accounts currently discussing the field of human organ transplantation and the several specialized areas such as that pertaining to the heart, kidney, liver, lung and cornea. These accounts were studied carefully in attempting to find certain trends and furnish certain data that may help substantiate conclusions and lead to the formulation of further recommendations and conclusions.

The Holy Bible, not considered to be a book of science or medicine, nor as a record of all historical events, still is THE BOOK and, as the inspired Word of God, is a living document which speaks to any and all ages — including this modern age of organ transplantation. Hence, quotations have been drawn from the Bible and allusions made to it as a primary source that has some light to shed upon the complicated subject. Since the Bible has not specifically dealt with human organ transplantation, often a passage has been quoted and left to make its impact upon the reader of this study as it may.

A full bibliography appears at the end of this study and to date is the most complete listing of the sources available. The writer is deeply indebted to Jacquelyn H. Hall, M.S., and David D. Swenson, M.D., for the annotated bibliography entitled PSYCHOLOGICAL AND SOCIAL ASPECTS OF HUMAN TISSUE TRANSPLANTATION.*

Considered also as primary source material is the correspondence between the writer and various physicians and surgeons throughout the United States and in some foreign countries. Among my noted correspondents are John H. Talbott, M.D., editor of the JOURNAL OF THE AMERICAN MEDICAL ASSOCIATION, who has granted permission for my quotation

*Public Health Service Publication No. 1838, published by the U.S. Department of Health, Education, and Welfare, U.S. Government Printing Office, Washington, D.C., 1968.

and use of published material of his journal, JAMA; Christiaan Barnard, M.D., first to perform a human heart transplant; Sister M. Josetta, O.S.F., who sent a copy of her master's thesis entitled, "The Morality of Heart Transplants," for my study and with permission to quote therefrom; Michael E. DeBakey, M.D., of the Baylor College of Medicine; Jacob Kline, Ph.D., professor and coordinator of the Biomedical Engineering Program of the University of Miami; Franz Stewart, M.D., editor of, THE JOURNAL OF THE FLORIDA MEDICAL ASSOCIATION; Dwight E. Harken, M.D., chief of the Thoracic Surgery Department at Peter Bent Brigham Hospital of Boston; The Reverend Ward, Chancery Librarian, Archdiocese of Miami; William E. Sanders, M.D., chief of the Heart Information Center, National Heart Institute, Bethesda, Maryland; John R. Pusey, attorney-at-law, Peoria, Illinois; Sister M. Canisia, O.S.F., administrator of St. Francis Hospital, Peoria, Illinois; Paul Ramsey, M.D., of the Department of Obstetrics and Gynecology at Georgetown University Hospital of Washington, D.C.; John J. Bergan, M.D., scientific director of the American College of Surgeons and National Institutes of Health, who recommended for my use the above mentioned Public Health Service Publication No. 1838.

To each of these and others, I owe a sincere debt of gratitude, for without their kind assistance, I could not have completed this manuscript.

I further express my appreciation to Doctor Warren Witus, who has encouraged me in this work.

I also express my appreciation to Ronald Clark, editor of the Akron BEACON JOURNAL and to Miss Dianne Coughlin for permission to quote from results of her research.

G.W.M.

CONTENTS

Page

Foreword by Dwight E. Harken vii

Preface ix

Introduction xiii

Chapter

    I. A Brief History of Organ Transplantation 3

    II. The Sanctity of Life and Dignity of Death 17

    III. Moral and Ethical Concerns: Donor 42

    IV. Moral and Ethical Concerns: Recipient 60

    V. Moral and Ethical Concerns: The Professionals 80

    VI. Moral and Ethical Concerns: The Hospital 88

    VII. Past, Present and Future 99

    VIII. Summary, Recommendations and Conclusions 111

Epilogue 119

Bibliography 121

Index 129

Moral and Ethical Implications of
HUMAN ORGAN TRANSPLANTS

"And the Lord God caused a deep sleep to fall upon Adam, and he slept: and He took one of his ribs, and closed up the flesh instead thereof; and the rib which the Lord God had taken from man, made He a woman, and brought her unto the man. And Adam said, This is now bone of my bones, and flesh of my flesh: she shall be called Woman, because she was taken out of Man."

(Genesis 2:21-23)

Chapter I

A BRIEF HISTORY OF
ORGAN TRANSPLANTATION

IT takes the unusual, the bizarre, the extraordinary to capture the attention of the general public. That
which is less sensational or which lacks the ability to capture
headlines will often go unnoticed and unchallenged. If the unusual
captures attention, it must be able to withstand whatever pressures
this attention may bring. With attention comes both praise and
criticism, acceptance and rejection, opportunity and challenge.

Actually, it was the announcement to the world of the first
human heart transplant done by Doctor Christiaan Barnard at
Groote Schuur Hospital in Capetown, South Africa, on December
3, 1967, that captured the attention of the world. Prior to this,
the transplantation of human organs drew little attention from the
public and was considered a matter between the medical profession and the patient.

One's concepts are colored by one's feelings and background.
Tradition, history, fact, and fiction all combine to determine how
one may feel about any given procedure. This is true in the field of
organ transplantation, but between the ultraemotionalism on the
one hand, and the complete lack of any concern on the other,
there appears to be a very broad area in which one may stand with
regards to the transplantation of human organs.

The history of organ transplantation actually spans several
years. When research seeks to establish definitely the time and
type of each organ transplant, problems arise due to failure in the
earliest beginnings to keep definite records. Doctor Phil Gunby,
head of the Public Information Center of the American Medical
Association, states that the center's records on transplants often
would not be final as they depended upon other media such as
clippings from newspapers and other such sources.

Dianne Coughlin of the BEACON JOURNAL, Akron, Ohio,

attempted to locate the source of the first transplants involving major organs. She states that she "ended up pretty much writing the history myself" (1). Her search took her to, among other places, the American College of Surgeons headquarters in Chicago; medical centers where transplants had taken place; the Human Kidney Transplant Registry of Boston, Massachusetts, and to the above-mentioned Public Information Center of the American Medical Association.

She found that there were conflicts regarding "firsts." For instance the American Medical Association and the Kidney Registry in Boston had listed the first kidney transplant as Richard Herrick of Northboro, Massachusetts. He received a kidney taken from his identical twin brother at Peter Bent Brigham Hospital in Boston on December 23, 1954. However, according to Miss Coughlin, the first transplantation of a human organ was that of a kidney performed on June 17, 1950, on a Mrs. Howard Tucker. The surgery was performed at Little Company of Mary Hospital in Chicago, Illinois. According to Doctor J. W. West, one of the surgeons on the team (Doctor West was still practicing in Chicago as of June, 1969), "This was the first transplant of any organ in history" (2).

Perhaps the reason for this mix-up was that the patient, Mrs. Howard Tucker, actually used the transplanted kidney for six months. It had been implanted to take the place of a completely diseased kidney. The other kidney, functioning at about 80 percent of normal, had not been removed. After the transplanted kidney failed six months later, it was removed. The patient was then kept alive for another five years on the partially functioning kidney. Her surgeon, Doctor West, stated that the transplanted kidney had helped the patient's own kidney "over a difficult transition" (3). This was credited as enabling the patient's own kidney to sustain the body on its own.

Due to Miss Coughlin's research, Doctor Gunby later located a write-up in a copy of the JOURNAL OF THE AMERICAN MEDICAL ASSOCIATION of 1950. "It's incredible," said Doctor Gunby. "They just present the case so matter-of-factly. And yet it appears to be the first organ transplant" (4). Doctor Gunby planned to add Mrs. Tucker's name to the list of transplants.

Perhaps the mistakes of the past helped to make more sure the preservation of data concerning later organ transplants. The National Heart Institute has kept a good record of heart transplants. The Human Kidney Transplant Registry Bank, located at Boston, will soon publish figures concerning transplantation.

Actually, some surgical and medical procedures have been classed as organ transplants when some medical authorities disagree as to their classification. Among the dubious "organ" procedures are skin grafts, blood transfusions, bone grafts and corneal transplants. The questionnaire sent to the physicians revealed that most did not consider these procedures as being legitimately classified as belonging to the organ transplantation area. At any rate, skin grafts, blood transfusions, bone grafts and corneal transplants have been going on for years. With the exception of the Jehovah's Witnesses, there seems to be no real theological objection to the use of any of these more acceptable forms of therapy today.

The Jehovah's Witnesses base their objection to blood transfusions upon such passages from the Bible as follows: Genesis 9:4; Leviticus 14:11-12, 14; Leviticus 7:26-27; Deuteronomy 12:23; Acts 15:19-20, 28-29; Acts 21:25. They are also reportedly in opposition to all forms of human organ transplantation. They believe that life is in the blood and that it is morally wrong to transplant life or any organ that may be associated with life. Their belief is extended to apply to the transplantation of human organs from a cadaver as well.

Whether procedures which involve the cornea, bone, skin, and others are actual organ transplants is best left to those of the medical profession. Whatever they may be called, it is known that these procedures are acceptable forms of treatment and are in wide use today. Blood transfusions are extremely prevalent and, as noted above, seem to raise no objection except by the one group mentioned. There are dangers in each of these procedures and most especially in the use of blood for transfusions. The watchful and skilled eye of the pathologist and his medical technologists have reduced the risks greatly.

There are risks, however, such as hepatitis, which can result from blood transfusions of blood taken from one who had the disease. Infections of various kinds can be passed through blood transfusions; the mismatching of blood can cause immediate death as, for example, if a person who has type A blood is given a transfusion from a type B person; more often, deaths occur which may be a result of cardiac failure when the transfusion is given too fast. The risks of blood transfusions have been minimized and seem to indicate that those certain cases which call for blood are of such importance as to warrant the procedure (5).

The transplantation of human organs has continued through a period which began in 1950. Miss Dianne Coughlin has researched the history from its earliest beginnings (6).

KIDNEY TRANSPLANTS

The first human organ transplant in history was done on June 17, 1950. The patient was a housewife, age 44. The surgery was performed by a team of surgeons which included Doctor J. W. West and others at Little Company of Mary Hospital in Chicago, Illinois. Since then, more than two thousand kidney transplants have been performed by many different surgeons in operating rooms throughout the United States and the world. The longest known survivor is a male identical twin who received his kidney in November, 1956, at Peter Bent Brigham Hospital in Boston. He was still living as of June, 1969. The average costs of kidney transplants reported by Mount Sinai Hospital of Cleveland is between $15,000 and $17,000. Peter Bent Brigham Hospital reports an average cost of $20,000 and Cleveland Clinic lists average costs at $10,000. The Medical College of Virginia, which has been the scene of over 160 kidney transplants, has no charges as the treatment is made possible under a grant from National Health Institutes.

LIVER TRANSPLANTS

The first recorded liver transplant was performed on March 1, 1963, on a three-year-old boy. It was done at the University of Colorado Medical Center in Denver. The child died on the operating table. Since then, forty-four have been done at various places and approximately thirteen of these have survived. The longest known survivor is a boy, age three, who received his transplant on February 9, 1968, at the University of Colorado Medical Center and is still alive. The leading center for liver transplants seems to be the University of Colorado Medical School which has been the scene of over twenty-nine such transplant procedures. The average cost as reported by the University of Colorado is $20,000 and up.

LUNG TRANSPLANTS

The first lung transplant was performed at the University of Mississippi Medical School on June 11, 1963, by Doctor James Hardy. The patient, a male, died just eighteen days later. A second transplant is worthy of a different type of "first." This was performed at the Tokyo Medical College in 1965 on a forty-four-year-old male patient. Listed as another "first," this particular surgical procedure involved the lobes. The patient was still alive as of June, 1969, but reportedly without lobes. There have been twenty lung transplants with one known long-term survivor. He is a twenty-three-year-old male who received lung transplant at the University of Ghent Hospital in Belgium on November 14, 1968. It is reported that his lung is functioning at approximately 60-to-70 percent of normal.

HEART TRANSPLANTS

The history-making first transplant of a human heart took place in Groote Schuur Hospital at Cape Town, South Africa, on December 3, 1967 (7). The surgeon in charge and the one credited with performing this feat was Doctor Christiaan Barnard. The patient was 55-year-old Louis Washkansky who lived for eighteen days while the world followed his progress with guarded optimism. He died of complications brought about as a result of rejection, the official diagnosis being pneumonia.

The second heart transplant performed on a human was done on December 6, 1967, by Doctor Kantrowitz at Maimonides Hospital in Brooklyn, New York. This patient, a male, lived for only six and a half hours. The seventeen-day-old infant had received the heart of a two-day-old male baby. The official cause of his death was listed as metabolic and respiratory acidosis.

The third human heart transplant is significant because of the length of time the recipient lived following the surgery. This, as the first, was performed by a team of surgeons headed by Doctor Christiaan Barnard. The recipient, Doctor Philip Blaiberg, who had retired from the practice of dentistry because of his heart condition, lived a total of 594 days. Operated on January 2, 1968, he died Sunday, August 17, 1969, at 7:40 P.M. His extended life is more significant when one considers that for several months he was able to live an almost normal life and was able to play tennis, swim and enjoy other hobbies and forms of recreation equally as strenuous. The cause of his death was due to complications from infections and rejection. It was listed as cardiac failure. Doctor Barnard told Mrs. Blaiberg, "Your husband is dying. I only want to ask you one thing. Was it all worth it for you?"

"Yes, you know it was worth it," she replied.

There have since been 134 cases of human heart transplants reported through July 1, 1969, and up to that time, there were still surviving thirty-one of the total number — or just slightly over 24 percent.

The official cause of death in thirty-five cases was rejection and acute rejection. In numerous other cases, the causes were due to infection, cardiac failure and pneumonia arising indirectly from rejection and its complication.

These above figures have changed since July 1, 1969, in numbers of transplants attempted, the number still surviving, and those who have died since July 1, 1969. This includes the world's longest living heart transplant patient, Doctor Philip Blaiberg. As previously noted, he died August 17, 1969, after 594 days.

OTHER TRANSPLANTS

The Spleen

There have been only seven attempts at transplanting the human spleen. The first was performed on a fifty-five-year-old male at the University of Colorado Medical Center on February 19, 1963. He died shortly after the surgery. Of these seven attempts, there are four surviving with a sixteen-year-old male patient being the longest still surviving. He received his new spleen on June 28, 1963, at the Colorado Medical Center. Though he still lives, it is reported that his physicians are not sure his new spleen is functioning as it should. The University of Colorado Medical Center has nearly dominated the research and performance in this area of organ transplantation, having transplanted six of the seven attempted. Costs are not available and the projected future of such transplants is not clear.

The Pancreas

On December 31, 1966, a thirty-two-year-old woman received the world's first reported pancreas transplant. This was done at the University of Minnesota Medical School in Minneapolis. She died four and a half months later. There have been a total number of seven attempts to transplant the human pancreas. There are three believed to be still surviving and the longest living patient is a twenty-nine-year-old man who received his new pancreas on May 25, 1968 in Rio de Janeiro, Brazil. The University of Minnesota leads the world in pancreas transplantation with five of the seven attempted. Due to the limited number of such organ transplantation, no estimate of costs is available.

The Thymus

The first and only transplant of the human thymus was performed on July 6, 1957, on an infant male at the University of Miami School of Medicine at Miami, Florida. He is still living at this writing. Due to the limited number of this type of transplant, no cost figures are available.

The Larynx

The first and only transplant involving the human larynx took place on January 10, 1969, on a sixty-two-year-old man at the

University Hospital, Ghent, Belgium. He is still living at this time and the successful operation resulted in two main functions — regaining the use of both voice and respiration through the new larynx. Doctor Paul Kluyskens, head of the Ear, Nose and Throat Department of Ghent University Clinic, was assisted in the four-hour operation by five other surgeons and three anesthetists. The limited number of such procedures has prevented the issuance of a cost analysis.

Hair Grafts

A recent headline grabber is the announcement that scalp transplants are now being performed. Though the procedure began back in 1959, it has only recently begun to come under public scrutiny. The operation actually is a series of procedures which are very expensive and cover a long period of time. There are two main ways of getting the job done. The first is a procedure called "spot-sodding." Here, the hair is removed in tiny plugs from the back of the head where the hair is thickest and then spot-sodded into the barren scalp. The cost is between $5 and $25 per six to sixteen hairs. The results seem to be gratifying, as a high number of these plugs grow well in their new beds.

Later, in 1961, Doctor Charles P. Vallis, instructor in plastic surgery at Tufts University in Boston, began what he termed "strip grafts." In this procedure, he removes quarter-inch-wide strips of scalp from the back part of the head and implants them along the place where the hairline once was. This "strip graft" is carefully stitched and usually begins to grow well in its new location. After the hairline has been firmly established, the other bare spots are then spot-sodded with plugs. According to Doctor Vallis, "The survival is excellent" (8).

Experiments in Sex Transplants

Some of the more outspoken critics of organ transplantation have voiced their objections on the basis of, "Where will it all end?" Not specifically objecting to that which is now being done, some fear the limits to which man may go in his quest for the prolongation of life and the finding of a fountain of youth that will enable him to enjoy the longer life. It appears that some of these fears may be well-grounded.

It is now reported that Russian doctors are experimenting with transplants involving the genital organs. The aim is plainly to extend the human sex life. The Soviet Public Health Minister, Doctor Boris Petroviskiy, has reported on attempts that now are being done on dogs, but experimental transplants of human sex organs may be undertaken within a few years (9).

Doctor Tommy N. Evans, head of Wayne State University's Department of Obstetrics and Gynecology, has predicted that within two years, ovary transplants may be a reality. This procedure would be aimed at those women whose ovaries had been removed by surgery or who had undergone an unusually early menopause (10).

Not lacking for possible recipients, Doctor Evans states that he already has on file the names of one hundred women who have applied for ovary transplants.

Questions concerning ovary transplants arise involving moral and ethical problems. Does the recipient bear children having the characteristics of the donor? What about the genes and the heredity? Whose baby is born?

Doctor Evans compares this procedure to artificial insemination. He points to the cases involving literally thousands of women who have carried and given birth to babies whose anonymous fathers had furnished the sperm which, in turn, was impregnated into the woman's womb. Although the child born with artificial insemination inherits the father's genes, it is argued that attempts are made to pick a donor who is much like the woman's husband in size, skin pigment, hair color and eyes.

The recipient of the ovary transplant would be matched with a donor whose characteristics were as much like her as possible.

Doctor James O'Leary, assistant professor of obstetrics and gynecology at the University of Miami School of Medicine, is experimenting with autotransplantation of the uterus, tubes and ovaries in rabbits and dogs. Doctor O'Leary states that he already has established a graft technique that is "satisfactory but requires further study" (11).

Another study into the miracle of birth involves the fertilization of human eggs in a test tube. Doctor Robert G. Edwards of Cambridge University has indicated that this same technique may be used to implant laboratory-fertilized embryos in women who are barren (12). In this procedure studied by the English physiologists, paternal relationship, both father and mother, would be precluded.

The American research in this area takes another turn. Doctor David Hume, chairman of the Department of Surgery at the Medical College of Virginia, states that some success in ovarian transplantation has been realized. He sees, in the English studies, that their plan would succeed in implanting an embryo into a woman and the baby would be neither of the mother nor the father. Of his studies, Doctor Hume states that when a woman is impregnated with eggs from another woman, the baby carried by her and given birth by her would actually be her husband's child though not her own. The baby's mother would actually be the woman whose ovary was transplanted.

There are dangers involved in the transplantation of ovarian tissue. "Technically, it can be done. It's a relatively simple process," states Doctor Hume. However, the danger is in the use of the immunosuppressive drugs which would be used, as in all transplant cases involving human organs. The danger, then, would be that the patient may develop infections and die as a result of the drugs, rather than the surgically implanted tissue.

In view of this danger, even Doctor Hume states, "It is not justifiable to do it. I would perform the operation only if a circumstance existed where a woman would commit suicide if she couldn't conceive" (13).

This seems to be a "luxury" that mankind really cannot afford nor really needs. In the case of vital organ transplantation, one may base his justifications on the fact that without the procedure, death is certain. However, in the case of a barren woman who "needs" the reassurance of giving birth to a baby, even though the baby is not her own, this seems a bit too risky for the amount of good that could possibly come from it.

In the case of artificial insemination, as it is being proposed for couples who are childless, it would seem that real problems could develop unless the couples would receive expert counseling and could come to a point of absolute agreement that they were mature enough to carry the responsibility for their decision.

It would seem that a much more morally acceptable manner of meeting the needs of childless couples could be found in the area of adoption. There are many children who have neither a father nor mother. They are already here. They need a normal home with mother and father. Other children are born out of wedlock and can be given up for adoption to childless couples who are looking for some child to brighten their own lives and one in whom they may invest themselves. In this particular matter, the writer stands firmly against attempts to transplant human embryos into infertile women.

Experiments in Brain Transplants

Those who have given their approval to vital organ transplantation have all stopped short of giving agreement to possible brain transplants. Others may be silent on this subject, believing that it is so utterly in vain, that none needs to even discuss it. But perhaps there is a need to discuss it, even in light of the evident impossibility of it all.

Doctor Boris Petroviskiy, Soviet Public Health Minister, has disclosed that Russian hospitals are carrying out partial brain transplants using dogs in the experiments. Some of the dogs have survived for as long as a week following these operations.

That men are experimenting in this area gives at least the remote idea that it may be possible. Things often thought to be impossible in the past are realities today. So, consider the moral and ethical implications should this come to pass. Should the brain become a transplantable organ, the donor would become the recipient. Should Mr. X die of a condition which apparently had not affected his brain, and this brain were to be transplanted into the vegetable-like body of Mr. Y, then Mr. Y, upon arising to the commands of this new brain, would be Mr. Y in physical appearance only, for his brain, the source of life, thought, movement, and memory, would be Mr. X. Thus, in being the donor of a brain, Mr. X would actually become the recipient of the body of Mr. Y. Hence, in actuality, this would be a body transplant, rather than that of a brain. Thus, Mr. Y, with all of his previous physical characteristics, would be in reality Mr. X. Upon arising from his hospital bed, he would return to the home of Mr. X; he would respond to the name of Mr. X. He would pass by the wife and children of Mr. Y and would physically embrace Mrs. X and call the X children as his own. He would not follow the profession or skill/trade that the body of Mr. Y once did, but would follow the work or profession of Mr. X.

In short, were the brain transplanted, life would go into the new body, for life now is believed to be in the brain. For theologians, the dilemma would be simply solved. Mr. X would be the living personality. Whatever his religious and spiritual persuasion were as Mr. X, these would continue in the body of Mr. Y. If all this sounds absurd, then perhaps it points up the impossibility of this particular transplant procedure.

Doctor Christiaan Barnard, who startled the world with the first transplant of the human heart, speaks cautiously in favor of the possibility of brain transplants. He admits that brain transplantation would pose serious technical problems, but suggests that spare-part surgery will reach the stage of body transplants. He said this latter development would occur ahead of brain transplants and evidentally believes this to be a real possibility (14).

Doctor Chisato Araki, who is the director of the Kitano Hospital at Osaka, Japan, a professor emeritus of Tokyo University, and a world-famous neurosurgeon, has discounted the idea of brain transplants. He said, "Since organ transplants, and in particular, heart transplants, have become a worldwide subject of conversation, considerable loose talk has been heard to the effect that brain transplants must also be possible. It seems that there are even surgeons who, half-serious perhaps, share such ideas. For my part, however, I consider them utterly impossible, whatever the means employed. I am not alone in this conviction: any neurosurgeon at all will tell you exactly the same thing" (15).

There are highly technical impossibilities of a brain transplant. The fact is that once the brain is cut off from the spinal cord and later sutured into the transplant, it would raise a real question about its ability to resume its functions. Another problem is the impossibility of regenerating the nerve fibers in the spinal cord. Another problem is that during experiments on the physiology of the brain, when an animal had its spinal cord severed at the upper end, life could not be maintained without continuous artificial respiration.

These and many other technical impossibilities have brought Doctor Araki to the position he has taken. However, there is still a greater problem. The donor of a transplanted brain, having died as an individual, would still be alive as his brain lived on. Thus, if his brain still functioned, it would be reasonable to suppose that such a man could not be said to have died yet. From this standpoint, according to Doctor Araki, the question of a brain transplant could not be raised at all (16).

On the basis of the variety of transplants discussed above, one must conclude that justification for them cannot always be that it was a matter of life and death. Often, certain transplants such as hair, skin, eye and bone may be for cosmetic purposes or to increase one's usefulness, and the question of life and death is not involved at all. This is not necessarily morally wrong. However, one must answer for himself the question as to whether his ultimate goal is worth the risks, the costs, the uncertainties, the agonies and the anxieties that are sure to come. When transplants are necessary to sustain or extend one's life, the recipient must face these risks, costs, uncertainties and decide for himself and his loved ones whether he thinks it is worth all that is involved. According to Mrs. Blaiberg, it *was* worth it.

But what is life? If it is shortened, is this always the worse thing that could happen? Can one really profit from a continuation on borrowed time? If given a new lease on life, will he return to the world some contribution that makes it all worth while?

Can one really measure life in terms of years? Consider Methuselah and Jesus Christ. Of the former, it is recorded that he lived 969 years (17). The only thing one knows about him is that he lived longer than anyone else. Of Jesus, who lived a scant thirty-three and a half years, the world still daily thinks and talks. His words, deeds, and acts are too numerous to be recorded. The apostle John wrote: "And there are also many other things which Jesus did, the which, if they should be written every one, I suppose that even the world itself could not contain the books that should be written" (18).

Life must be defined and qualified. It must be evaluated by the contributions it makes and can never be counted merely in terms of length of time.

NOTES

1. Beacon Journal, Akron, Ohio. June 1, 1969. Mrs. Dianne Coughlin, Staff Writer. Used by permission.
2. Ibid.
3. Ibid.
4. Ibid.
5. These risks and possibilities have been verified by Doctor William Riemer, chief of pathology at Baptist Hospital of Miami, Florida.
6. Op. Cit., Beacon Journal.
7. National Heart Institute: Cardiac Replacement. Ad Hoc Task Force Report. Washington, U.S. Government Printing Office, October, 1969, pp. 65-75. Used by permission.
8. The Miami News. February 8, 1969, p. 5B, and January 22, 1970.
9. Ibid., September 25, 1969. p. 8A.
10. The Miami Herald. April 6, 1969, p. 20A. Detroit Free Press. Used by permission.
11. The Miami News. March 10, 1969.
12. Ibid.
13. Ibid.
14. Ibid., October 13, 1969, p. 3A.
15. Medical Tribune. New York, April 21, 1969.
16. Ibid.
17. The Holy Bible. Genesis 5:27.
18. Ibid., John 21:25.

Chapter II

THE SANCTITY OF LIFE AND DIGNITY OF DEATH

THE sanctity of life and the dignity of death is a right due every human being by our Divine Creator – God, who is the author of all life. There is a time to live and a time to die. Without being fatalistic about it, simply put, a person is born, continues in life for a time, and then dies. There have been many attempts by people to realize immortality while in the flesh, upon this earth, within one's lifetime. However, although there are many varying degrees in the length of human life, all have died. Job grappled with this problem (1):

> Man that is born of woman is of few days and full of trouble. He comes forth like a flower, and withers; he flees like a shadow, and continues not. And dost thou open thy eyes upon such a one and bring him into judgment with thee? Who can bring a clean thing out of an unclean? There is not one. Since his days are determined, and the number of his months is with thee, and thou has appointed his bounds that he cannot pass, look away from him, and desist, that he may enjoy like a hireling, his day.

The Preacher, Ecclesiastes, also struggled with this problem (2):

> For everything there is a season, and a time for every matter under heaven:
> a time to be born, and a time to die;
> a time to plant, and a time to pluck up what is planted;
> a time to kill, and a time to heal;
> a time to break down, and a time to build up;
> a time to weep, and a time to laugh;
> a time to mourn, and a time to dance;
> a time to cast away stones, and a time to gather stones together;
> a time to embrace, and a time to refrain from embracing;
> a time to seek, and a time to lose;
> a time to keep, and a time to cast away;
> a time to rend, and a time to sew;
> a time to keep silence, and a time to speak;

17

a time to love, and a time to hate;
a time for war, and a time for peace.
What gain has the worker from his toil?
I have seen the business that God has given to the sons of men to be
busy with.
He has made everything beautiful in its time;
also He has put eternity into the man's mind, yet so that he cannot
find out what God has done from the beginning to the end. I know
that there is nothing better for them than to be happy and enjoy
themselves as long as they live; also that it is God's gift to man that
every one should eat and drink and take pleasure in all his toil. I know
that whatever God does endures for ever; nothing can be added to it,
nor anything taken from it; God has made it so, in order that men
should fear before Him.

The sanctity of life does not end with the death of one in this world. In these same two references, both Job and Ecclesiastes have jarred the door ever-so-slightly open to the concept of eternal life — life beyond the bounds and limitations of this physical existence experienced in this world. Job asked, "If a man die, shall he live again?" And he answered his own question, "All the days of my appointed time will I wait, till my change come" (3). Ecclesiastes stated it thusly, "He has made everything beautiful in its time; also he has put eternity into man's mind . . ." (4). Jesus expressed the sanctity of life by relating it to a trust in Him, "I am come that they might have life, and that they might have it more abundantly (5).

In recording the sacred history of man's first beginnings, the act of life itself is attributed to a divine work of God: "And the Lord God formed man of the dust of the ground, and breathed into his nostrils the breath of life; and man became a living soul" (6).

That man's life is sacred and should be accepted so by others is best seen in the fury of God as found in the first recorded act of murder: "Cain rose up against Abel his brother, and slew him . . . and he (God) said, 'What hast thou done? The voice of thy brother's blood crieth unto me from the ground. And now art thou cursed from the earth, which hath opened her mouth to receive thy brother's blood from thy hand; when thou tillest the ground, it shall not henceforth yield unto thee her strength; a fugitive and a vagabond shalt thou be in the earth" (7).

DEFINITION OF LIFE

Difficult in most cases and nearly impossible in some is the task of giving a simple definition to a word. There are many levels in a definition, beginning on a bare, simple surface and going to great depths. Such is the case of the word "life." Simply defined, life is that property of plants and animals which makes it possible for them to take in food, get energy from it, grow, adapt themselves to their surroundings, and reproduce their kind (8). But there are those who could just barely qualify here who really are more existing than living. Life among humans is the most sacred of possessions. Thus, the sixth commandment is expressed firmly in the negative: "Thou shalt not kill" (9). This is God's commandment for the preservation of the right of man to live. Life is such a priceless pearl! For the preservation of human life, all of science, medicine, theology, and other such philosophies unite.

What, then, is life, and how shall it be defined?

Natural

Natural life may be defined as a series of adjustments and adaptations. It is the ability of one, plant or animal, to live within its own environment with a naturalness unaffected by any extraordinary stimuli. For want of something better, one may divide life into three basic types.

1. Organic and Biological

Here, one, whether plant or animal, has life if there is the apparent ability to take nourishment, grow, and adapt to its environment. This definition is merely the opposite of that which is and has been inorganic or inanimate. Life thus defined may be applied to the one-celled, tiny amoeba. Though little more than a blob of microscopic nucleated protoplasm, this tiny animal can lay claim upon this definition of life.

2. Intellectual and Emotional

Here, life takes on more meaning. One has the ability to think, learn and develop relationships. Though somewhat broadly applicable to certain animals, this second definition is understood to be reserved for human beings. Man is an intelligent being. He has the ability to feel various emotions, and to become a creative, thinking and participating member of the society of which he is a part. He can live in and adapt to the environment in which he finds himself. Not merely fitted to adapt to his environment, man, in this definition of life, can actually adapt his environment to his manner of living. Man can explore, learn, grow toward maturity, and become conscious of his and others' presence and needs. He can interrelate and interact with his fellow man. Life on this plane is vastly superior to a mere organic or biological concept of life.

3. Spiritual

The human, and only the human, was created in the divine image of God. Mankind was a creation of the Creator in a way much different than were the plants and lower animals of the world. These were created by a good God, in an act of His own choice. Of these plants it was written, "Let the earth bring forth grass, the herb yielding seed, and the fruit tree yielding fruit after his kind, whose seed is in itself, upon the earth: and it was so" (10). Of the fish and the fowl and their creation it was written, "Let the waters bring forth abundantly the moving creature that hath life, and fowl that may fly above the earth in the open firmament of heaven. And God created great whales, and every living creature that moveth, which the waters brought forth abundantly, after their kind, and every winged fowl after his kind: and God saw that it was good" (11). And of the animals and their creation it was written, "Let the earth bring forth the living creature after his kind, cattle, and creeping thing, and beast of the earth after his kind: and it was so" (12). But of man, God's highest creation, it was written, "Let us make man in our image, after our likeness: and let them have dominion over the fish of the sea, and over the fowl of the air, and over the cattle, and over all the earth, and over every creeping thing that creepeth upon the earth" (13). There is the supreme concept of life. Man is a living spirit; a personality that is made to fellowship with the divine.

Man is organic — he is body; man is intellectual — he has a mind; man is spirit — he can commune with God and live in peace with Him. Thus, "life," at its highest definition, is the ability to live and function creatively and meaningfully with intelligence and responsibility, and in a spirit of fellowship with Almighty God.

Artificial

Artificial life is synthetic, unnatural, feigned and unreal. Such mechanical devices or uses of certain medicinal stimulants to create or maintain a semblance of life is not to be confused with the definitions of life given above. There are instances where the definitions of life just described (i.e., organic and biological, intellectual and emotional, and spiritual) can be had only by use of artificial aids such as a pacemaker to assist one's failing heart. One's use of "artificial" means that helping to sustain life and allowing for a meaningful, conscious awareness of life's challenges and opportunities, is not morally wrong. Medical authorities have been helping people find useful expressions in extended life by artificial means for years. But physicians do not wish to be classed as mere mechanics who desperately fight to prolong life by artificial means. Once hope for a meaningful participation in life is no longer possible, extraordinary means should be discontinued. They are interested in the prevention of untimely or premature death, and to them, all society is indebted. Their combined contribution has extended the life expectancy from approximately forty years at the turn of the century to over seventy years at the present time (14).

How long should the body be kept alive by artificial means? In a terminally ill patient who has no chance of recovery, this is not an easy question to answer. The layman may ask the physician if he has the right to keep a person from dying. The physician may answer that he has taken an oath to preserve life and alleviate human suffering. But what are the alternatives open to the physician where these two parts of his oath come into conflict? There is the terminal patient, dying with incurable cancer. The relief of this one's suffering may take precedence over the preservation of life. There are certainly other cases not classed as terminal, in which the physician is more concerned with preserving life than in relieving suffering (15). There invarably will come case histories from the files of reputable physicians producing evidence of those certain "terminal," vegetable-like cases that make a remarkable recovery. These cases are unusual, exceptional and largely unexplainable. They should not be taken as absolute and final criteria to justify excessive and prolonged use of artificial equipment to sustain a semblance of life. However, if there is a serious doubt as to how long one should rely on artificial means, then an electroencephalograph (EEG) can be run, and when shown to be flat for two hours, the machine can be turned off as the patient is dead (16).

Sometimes the patient who is absolutely dependent upon a machine for his life will request the discontinuance of it. This he may do either out of deference to his family, who may be hard-pressed financially, or "having gotten his house in order," he may just be ready to welcome death as a release and chance to enter the new life of eternity.

One clergyman anonymously answering the question – "Do you believe it is morally wrong to sustain life by artificial means?" – put his words in a fresh and pointed manner. He wrote: "When God takes my hands in death, I pray no man will hold my heels." He went on to qualify his answer, "By this I mean simply that I believe it is morally wrong to sustain mere existence physiologically." In contrast to this rather mature outlook, a hospital chaplain responded with a brief case study in which he told of a fifty-three-year-old male patient who had become emotionally attached to the machine during hemodialysis treatments over a four-year period. There were many complications produced in the life patterns of this close-knit actively religious family.

Another hopeless patient, Ron Frederickson of Minneapolis, Minnesota, had been living for three years with the aid of a kidney machine. He and his physicians knew that the diabetic condition which had caused his kidney disease would be fatal. So, the patient one day signed a waiver removing himself from further treatment. He told his wife that he was "ready to die." He told a reporter from the Minneapolis Star, Jim Klobucher, "I tell you I'm not afraid of death. Do you know how I feel? I'm kind of excited.

Some time ago I became what I think is a real Christian. I now really believe this is just a beginning" (17). A week after he discontinued treatments, he died. A week after he discontinued treatments, he began to live anew.

The cost of "machine life" is astronomical. No one likes to put a price tag on life, but it is there — undeniably so. Consider the price of life tied to a kidney machine: The first year bill for home dialysis, including $3,000 to $4,000 to purchase the artificial kidney machine and fees for training a member of the family to operate it, totals about $10,000; from then on, it costs from $3,000 to $5,000 a year to maintain the machine and buy the necessary chemicals (18). Many people could not afford this expense.

The other alternative would be a kidney transplant. There are risks. Tissues must match or rejection will occur. Hospital and physicians must be paid. The cost of a kidney transplant is approximately $15,000 to $17,000 and could go as high as $20,000. Federal grants and private donations are dwindling as more and more people are seeking to maintain life by this artificial means.

The truth is that in many cases, life can be maintained by artificial means. It is costly, painful, temporary, and produces anxiety. Is it worth it? Only the person and his particular circumstance can clearly answer. The theologian who believes in life eternal can applaud the courage and the testimony of the Ron Fredericksons. The theologian, while lauding the efforts of medical science, feels life can be unreasonably prolonged.

DEFINITIONS OF DEATH

Death appears to be more easily defined than life. Webster defines "death" as a permanent cessation of all vital functions: the end of life; the cause or occasion of loss of life; the state of being dead (19). If one is content to accept these as sufficient definitions of death without going into the deeper, more involved theological, legal and philosophical implications, then for him, definition of death is fairly simple. When life ceases, death is a reality. There are no problems, either metaphysically, medically, or scientifically. However, can one accept death so easily defined?

To say that a plant, animal, or human is dead when no evidences of life are present, is lacking — for there are people walking around today who for a span of time had no visible evidences of life. They were not dead and are not dead now. There was a time when a medical doctor could listen for a moment or so to a patient's chest with his stethoscope and upon hearing no heartbeat, he could then declare the patient to be medically dead. Today, with the age of human organ transplantation fully upon us, this is no longer true — especially if the deceased is to be a donor of some vital organ.

The definition of death now has become a rather involved process and finds itself being defined at several different levels. To many in the medical profession, the involvement of other disciplines in the definitions of death is an encroachment. Doctor Christiaan Barnard, speaking to a group of physicians and others in Miami, Florida, stated, "I cannot understand why the world now questions the doctor's ability to diagnose death now that transplants are being done (20). He was sincere and honest in his feelings. When one realizes that it still is the physician's duty to diagnose and pronounce death, it is understandable that the medical world is upset. But then, with the introduction to the world of vital organ transplantation, and this often from another human donor, it would seem that the physician would realize and accept the fact that death takes on new meanings. Many physicians, perhaps most, do realize this and are in agreement that new definitions of death must be made.

The editor of HOSPITALS, journal of the American Hospital Association, James E. Hague, has written (21):

> Buck-passing is the domain of well over 99 percent of humanity. That statistic isn't official, but it's pretty obvious when a fascinating, terrifying, inexorably compelling decision has to be made — for example: Who (God or a man) must carry the responsibility for a life when a heart, still pumping, is cut out of one human chest and invested in another? Such a responsibility is an agonizing cup; accepting it commits one to an awsome chain of admissions — about God, one's origin, fate, the future, the soul, and man's relationship to man. Formidable. For some reason we have bestowed on the surgeon the right, or the guilt, of these momentous decisions.

Yet another decision: Is the mystique of the heart based in something other than romantic literature? More than just an unanswered question, this has to be a decision. Like the other questions about death, legality, and moral responsibility, this one must be answered and the answer must be agreed upon before we can proceed with confidence. Before hearts, there was little suspicion of transplantation ethics. A transplanted cornea and a skin graft were celebrated as marvels of the new medical technology, proof that man is indeed ascending to the point of ultimate cosmic perfection. But with hearts came bounding back primeval fear, and now we have to start again, this time with honesty lest the fear visit us again in a worse form . . . Eventually the ethical and moral problems of organ transplantation may be solved wisely, by application of the minds of surgeons *and* administrators *and* nurses *and* attorneys *and* clergymen *and* the rest of us whose responsibility the solution certainly is.

Legal

It is given that the pronouncement of death has always been the physician's responsibility and should remain so. Previously, the physician had proceeded upon the theory that death was thought of as cessation of physical life. Some indications were the stoppage of the circulation of blood and other vital signs. Today, new definitions must be reached in light of the availability of techniques capable of prolonging the life of hopelessly ill patients indefinitely. The rapid strides made recently in human organ transplantation has emphasized the need to reexamine definitions of death.

The creation of the Uniform Anatomical Gift Act, which has been approved by the American Bar Association, the American Medical Association, and has been adopted by most of the fifty states, has been of extreme value.

A statement on death was issued by the twenty-second World Medical Assembly in Sydney, Australia, in August, 1968. The statement is as follows (22):

The determination of the time of death is in most countries the legal responsibility of the physician and should remain so. Usually he will be able without special assistance to decide that a person is dead employing the classical criteria known to all physicians.

Two modern practices in medicine however have made it necessary to study the question of the time of death further: (1) the ability to maintain by artificial means the circulation of oxygenated blood through tissues of the body which may have been irreversibly injured, and (2) the use of cadaver organs such as hearts or kidneys for transplantation.

A complication is that death is a gradual process at the cellular level with tissues varying in their ability to withstand deprivation of oxygen. But clinical interest lies not in the state of preservation of isolated cells but in the fate of a person. Here the point of death of the different organs is not so important as the certainty that the process has become irreversible by whatever techniques of resuscitation that may be employed. This determination will be based on clinical judgment supplemented if necessary by a number of diagnostic aids of which the electroencephalograph is currently the most helpful.

However, no single technological criterion is entirely satisfactory in the present state of medicine nor can any one technological procedure be substituted for the overall judgment of the physician. *If transplantation of an organ is involved, the decision that death exists should be made by two or more physicians and the physicians determining the moment of death should in no way be immediately concerned with the performance of the transplantation.*

In determining the legal time of death when there will be transplantation of vital human organs, there is set as the final criteria, the death of the brain. Definition of brain death has been studied and certain criteria for determining this has been established by the Ad Hoc Committee of the Harvard Medical School. These criteria include (1) unreceptivity and unresponsitivity, (2) no movements or breathing, (3) no reflexes, and (4) flat EEG.

Each of these criteria is explained in detail, including the fact that the EEG should record at twice the normal rate again, with appropriate measures taken to detect artifactual activity. Appropriate measures to ensure that the coma is not due to hypothermia or drug intoxication are required. All of these criteria are to be reexamined twenty-four hours later and if all of these are still obtained, the brain is defined as permanently nonfunctional and the person is defined as dead, though other organs may continue to function (23).

While there is a consensus that brain death is the acceptable definition of death, it is interesting to note that criteria for the determination of brain death has not been fully agreed upon by clinicians and laymen.

The Ad Hoc Committee of the Harvard Medical School noted:

> The legal system of the United States is greatly in need of the kind
> of analysis and recommendations for medical procedures in cases of
> irreversible brain damage as described. At present, the law of the
> United States, in all fifty states and in the federal courts, treats the
> question of human death as a question of fact to be decided in every
> case. When any doubt exists, the courts seek medical expert
> testimony concerning the time of death of the particular individual
> involved. However, the law makes the assumption that the medical
> criteria for determining death are settled and not in doubt among
> physicians. Furthermore, the law assumes that the traditional method
> among physicians for determination of death is to ascertain the
> absence of all vital signs. In the few modern court decisions involving
> a definition of death, the courts have used the concept of the total
> cessation of all vital signs (24).

This legal definition is not helpful in cases involving human
organ transplantation and is not consistent, either, with current
medical understanding. Death of the whole body does not occur at
the same time, and yet, the determination of the exact time of
death may have major legal and financial consequences for the
surviving family. The law still depends upon the consensus of
medical opinion for a definition of death. If there is no serious
disagreement among members of the medical profession, legislation to determine and define death by law is not probable.

For the theologian, the opinion of reputable physicians using
whatever means at their disposal, and following the generally
acceptable criteria for death, is sufficient. In the area of
pronouncement of death, the theologian rightly defers to the
physician. The moral and ethical implications here are that the
physician cannot kill one patient for the purposes of saving the life
of another. The end does not justify this action and it is believed
they would not contemplate such action.

Medical — Clinical

In discussing the legal definitions of death, some of the medical
terminology has been touched upon. It has been previously stated
that it seems death would be more easily defined than life. But in

looking at the problem in depth, it is seen to be very difficult, indeed. It is now known, since the transplantation of vital human organs has become a reality, that disagreement as to the time of death may be increased among physicians. At the twenty-first annual meeting of the American Academy of Neurology, it was found there was not complete agreement among neurologists as to how to determine the true time of death. A group of four leading neurologists reported their findings and recommendations to this convention. They had recommended a wait of twenty-four hours after the first recording of irreversible coma by the EEG. This wait, if enforced, would adversely affect the transplantation of vital human organs.

The reason for the 24-hour delay was explained by Doctor Robert S. Schwat, a member of the committee. He said that the wait would give the necessary time to make blood analysis to determine if the coma was truly irreversible − as might be indicated in overdoses of drugs − or whether it was treatable by blood purification procedures.

The committee had sent out questionnaires to 2,600 neurologists and others expert in the field of electroencephalography. The physicians reported twenty-three survivals, mostly from overdoses of drugs. Some, however, were blamed on inadequate uses of the electroencephalographies (25).

Differing from the conclusions of this committee of four, representing the Academy of Neurology, was the Ad Hoc Committee of the American Electroencephalographic Society. After examining the literature dealing with certain cases of recovery after having shown "flat" EEG's, this committee concluded that not one of those who recovered had in truth experienced real isoelectric EEG's. In fact, they found that the longest period of isoelectric recording with eventual recovery, where there was no excludable circumstances, was forty-five minutes. Even with excludable circumstances, the longest recovery was 120 minutes.

The Ad Hoc Committee of the American EEG Society failed to reveal a single instance of a truly isoelectric EEG with recovery in a patient who was not under anesthetic doses of central nervous system depressants. Therefore, this committee agreed that the recommended required duration of the complete state of brain death for twenty-four hours is not justified (26). On the basis of their study, this Ad Hoc Committee concluded that a person should be considered dead according to central nervous system indicators if the clinical and electroencephalographic criteria are present continuously for a period of two hours. They also pointed out that adherence to that guideline would have prevented a majority of the heart transplantations that have been performed (27). One may have been convinced thoroughly that two hours of a flat EEG is long enough before one is declared dead.

Then comes the added comment of Doctors C. M. Robert and D. P. Becker who, while questioning the twenty-four-hour wait before certifying death when organ transplantation is planned, feel that if the situation does not demand an immediate decision, an observation period of from twenty-four to forty-eight hours is reasonable (28). What they seem to be saying is that a flat EEG for two hours is enough to certify death of a patient. An organ can be transplanted after this period of observation, but longer periods of observation may be considered reasonable if no transplant is to be done.

The question must be raised — if two hours is long enough to certify death with an organ transplant in mind, why is it "reasonable" to wait from twenty-four to forty-eight hours longer if no organ is to be used? If a person is dead enough to be declared dead in two hours of a flat EEG, he is dead enough not to be observed for twenty-four to forty-eight hours longer with or without a transplant in view. It would seem that the extra hours of "observation" would add to the cost and lead into prolonged agony and grief for the family. If there is a doubt that the person is dead in two hours of a flat EEG, then removal of the organ would be premature. The question is not whether two hours wait is long enough, but rather, why extend it for twenty-four or forty-eight more hours?

The greatest problem created by heart transplantation involves the donor. He must be protected against a premature pronouncement of death. Physicians and the institutions in which they work have recognized the possibility of a "conflict of interest" that may be involved if the same physician cared for both the donor and the recipient. "The patient must be absolutely sure that his doctor does not become his executioner, and that no definition authorizes him to ever become one. His right to this certainty is absolute" (29).

The need for guidelines as to the pronouncement of the time of death has resulted in an ad hoc committee formed in Pittsburgh, Pa., in September, 1968, under the sponsorship of the Institute of Forensic Science in the Duquesne University School of Law. This committee was organized to develop a protocol for the determination of death by physicians and to outline certain medico-legal principles involved in human organ transplantation. They concluded after many meetings by offering the following protocol (30):

1. Documentation of death.
    1) Lack of responsiveness to internal and external environment.
    2) Absence of spontaneous breathing movements for three minutes, in absence of hypocarbia and breathing room air.
    3) No muscular movements, with generalized flacidity, and no evidence of postural activity or shivering.
    4) Reflexes and responses:
        (1) pupils fixed and dilated, nonreactive to strong light stimuli;
        (2) corneal reflexes absent;
        (3) supraorbital or other pressure response absent (both pain response and decerebrate posturing);
        (4) absence of snouting and sucking responses;
        (5) no reflex response to upper airway stimulation;
        (6) no reflex response to lower airway stimulation;
        (7) no ocular response to ice water stimulation of inner ear (caloric test);
        (8) no deep tendon reflexes;
        (9) no superficial reflexes;
        (10) no plantar responses.
    5) Falling arterial pressure without support by drugs or other means.
    6) Isoelectric   electroencephalogram   (in   absence   of

hypothermia, anesthetic agents, and drug intoxication), recorded spontaneously and during auditory and tactile stimulation. (Multiple recordings totaling at least ninety minutes, using a standard number of diagnostic electrodes with maximun allowable interelectrode distances. Part of recording at full gain. External artifacts and EKG excluded by use of right-hand electrode.)

   7) A note detailing these observations should be made in chart at time of first determination of irreversible coma.

2. Certification of death.

   1) Criteria "a" through "f" should be present for at least two hours before death is certified.

   2) Death should be certified and recorded in the patient's chart by two physicians other than the physicians of a potential organ recipient.

In view of this very thorough and in-depth definition of death, it would seem that the donor of a vital human organ would be adequately protected against any premature certification of death and would therefore be considered a cadaver donor. For theologians, this should cause no difficulty for it is written: "For we know that if our earthly house of this tabernacle were dissolved, we have a building of God, an house not made with hands eternal in the heavens . . . whilst we are at home in the body, (alive) we are absent from the Lord: . . . We are confident, I say, and willing rather to be absent from the body, (dead) and to be present with the Lord" (31). The physicians and attorneys have seen fit to write hard and fast rules to be followed in the death of one person and the possible transplantation of vital human organs to another, thus protecting both donor and recipient.

EUTHANASIA

The practice of euthanasia is illegal. Need one say more on the subject? Before deciding, it would be wise to define the word. WEBSTER'S UNABRIDGED DICTIONARY defines "euthanasia" as "a painless, happy death." It comes from a combination of two Greek words meaning "well" and "death." Defined further, it is an easy and painless death; a peaceful manner of dying; it is an act or method of causing death painlessly, so as to end suffering; advocated by some as a way to deal with victims of incurable diseases (32).

If one takes the first definition, "easy and painless death," or "a peaceful manner of dying," then illegal or not, both physician and theologian and all others would be guilty — for the physician often gives treatment both medically and surgically to ease death and make it more peaceful and less painful. The theologian often prays to a kind and merciful God and implores that He will not permit one to suffer beyond his capacity to bear. When convinced that one is terminal, the theologian seeks to prepare one for death and prays that it shall not be a long, drawn-out and agonizing experience. But is this really euthanasia?

Looking at the more involved second definition, "an act or method of CAUSING death painlessly, so as to end suffering," we see that the key word is "causing." Therefore, euthanasia may be defined as "mercy killing." Disciplines and cultures unite to condemn such. Legal restrictions forbid it. Theology almost universally prohibits it. Medical men fear and flee from the practice of it like it were a plague, and to them, it is worse.

But to what extent is it being practiced, permitted or tolerated? Again the definition one chooses is vitally important. Consider one of the oldest written regulations governing the ethics of a profession, the Oath of Hippocrates (33).

I swear by Apollo the Physician, and Aesculapius, and Hygeia, and Panacea, and all the gods and all the goddesses — and I make them my judges — that this mine oath and this my written engagement I will fulfil so far as power and discernment shall be mine.

Him who taught me this art I will esteem even as I do my Parents; he shall partake of my livelihood and, if in want, shall share my goods. I will regard his issue as my brothers, and will teach them this art without fee or written engagement if they shall wish to learn it.

I will give instruction by precept, by discourse, and in all other ways, to my own sons, to those of him who taught me, to disciples bound by written engagement and sworn according to medical law, and to no other person.

So far as power and discernment shall be mine, I will carry out regimen for the benefit of the sick, and will keep them from harm and wrong. To none will I give a deadly drug, even if solicited, nor offer counsel to such an end; likewise to no woman will I give a destructive suppository; but guiltless and hallowed will I keep my life and mine art. I will cut no one whatever for the stone, but will give way to those who work at this practice.

Into whatsoever houses I shall enter I will go for the benefit of the sick, holding aloof from all voluntary wrong and corruption, including venereal acts upon the bodies of females and males whether free or slaves. Whatsoever in my practice or not in my practice I shall see or hear, amid the lives of men, which ought not to be noised abroad – as to this I will keep silence, holding such things unfitting to be spoken.

And now if I shall fulfil this oath and break it not, may the fruits of life and of art be mine, may I be honored of all men for all time; the opposite, if I shall transgress and be foresworn.

In this, we see that the physician has taken an oath regarding his own personal and professional conduct as a physician. Would it be an oversimplification to reduce this to the phrase, "If one cannot do good, one should do no harm."? This seems to be what the discussion of euthanasia is all about. One may not DO anything to CAUSE or HASTEN death. Is he, then, duty-bound above all else to do anything and everything to prolong life? Is there a difference in causing death and needlessly prolonging life? There seems to be a difference. In injecting a substance to hasten or cause death, one has taken a life and this is murder. Whatever the motive – to relieve suffering, to end agony – one still has induced death. But if one withholds a substance, an artificial stimulant or drug, or a procedure, is he guilty of taking a life? One's answer here will be the real definition for him of euthanasia. The theologian has mixed emotions and varied instructions here. It is all bound up in what is meant by life and what is meant by death. Discussed earlier, it is hoped one may review and then make his own determination.

Should the law governing euthanasia withhold a person's right to die in dignity? Do physicians resist death to their patients so arduously because of fear of breaking the law concerning euthanasia? Do they resist death because of other reasons? As one medical doctor put it, "Physicians are frequently responsible for this frenetic and fearful form of ending (whereby death is "eased" into by slow and painful steps) and the ill are occupied by symptoms or the rigors of treatment and have little or no opportunity for quiet contemplation. Bound by a misapplied duty as healers, they resist death, often more vigorously than does the patient" (34). Should the patient have not only the right to die in dignity, but also to *know* that he is going to die? What right does the physician have to withhold the information from the very one whose privilege and right it is to know? If the family insists on compelling the physician not to tell the patient the truth, should he bow to this pressure when he does not bow to other pressures which the family often tries to assert in order to influence his medical judgment? Should he welcome the pressure to give him this out? To tell or not to tell? − that is the question. However, the decision not to tell should be the exception, rather than the rule.

True, there are occasions if the news is broken to a patient that he is going to die, that it may cause such real trauma as to have warranted its being withheld. But then, whose responsibility is it to know of this likelihood? It would be the physician's duty to know or at least anticipate such a response, and he may (and should) employ the counsel of the patient's spiritual advisor, minister, priest, rabbi or hospital chaplain. More often than not, the physician today will be straightforward and candid with his patient.

There are many reasons in favor of this approach and, in general, they far outweigh the reasons for not telling him. The patient who knows he is dying will have the opportunity to discuss his problems, personal, or otherwise, with his spiritual advisor. He has the knowledge that will help to remove barriers in communication with others, especially in regard to his family. He can summon, from a distance, his loved ones and friends. He can have the pleasure of his loved one's company without the embarassing, "I know, but you don't know I know," and "I know you know, but you don't know I know you know," and other such cat and mouse forms of evading reality. Another reason the patient needs to know the truth about his condition is that it allows him to bring into play his vast abilities and resources physically, mentally and spiritually to combat his disease and/or to face it realistically, with maturity and in dignity.

Theological Implications

In the practice of euthanasia as defined above, so as to be illegal, none would prefer to assume the liability for their decision of advising it. If one would be hesitant to advise euthanasia, would it not be for fear of prosecution? In the decision as to who is to live, are there so many who are brave enough to volunteer to make this choice? Actually, when life of a human is involved, is it not equally difficult to choose the one to live as it may be to choose to allow another to die? In the whole area of vital human organ transplantation, this question is found to be in the very center.

Some have declared that the speeding up of a donor's death, when death is positively inevitable, may be justified if the transplant provides another human with the opportunity for life. Such a conclusion is consistent with the thought of Joseph Fletcher in his reported sponsorship of euthanasia (35). The decision not to use artificial means to sustain life has been called by some a "bringing death about lefthandedly" (36). In arriving at a decision not to let it all hang on chance, one has employed, if rather broadly, the concept of euthanasia.

Consider this hypothetical case. Suppose a very high-ranking government official suffers a serious coronary attack. He needs a heart transplant to stay alive. These questions are raised: May not even the most reputable physician be tempted to let treatment of a critically ill patient go lacking in preference to one who may be deemed more worthy? May not others who think of themselves as less worthy to live, less able to make a vital contribution to the world, step forward and volunteer their heart in order to spare the life of a world leader?

Such actually happened during the critical illness of the late President Dwight Eisenhower. There were numerous people who indicated they would gladly donate their heart to spare his life. Noble and martyr-like were their intentions, but would they have really proved anything? Would they all have been so willing if their tissues matched and surgery was scheduled? Some may have.

Would this have been voluntary death-suicide on the volunteer's part? If medical authorities and, indeed, the patient himself had agreed to such a noble sacrifice, would they be guilty of practicing euthanasia by consent? The President is reported to have personally ruled out any thought of a heart transplant. He died, nobly, his own death. He had not wished to even consider such offers on the part of others, whether offered in jest, for publicity or in earnest.

In further considering the concept of death with dignity, there should be a clear distinction made between what has been called "positive euthanasia" and the oath to which the physician subscribes not to take life (37). There is a difference. In the Oath of Hippocrates quoted earlier, the physician has sworn that he will "give no deadly drug to anyone if asked, nor suggest any such counsel" (38).

Positive euthanasia, then, may be defined as the overt, willful taking of life by actually giving some medication or some injection that will bring death to the patient. This is illegal, immoral, unethical and unwarranted in any case and under any circumstance. The withholding of artificial means of whatever nature so that the act of dying is not prolonged, and when damage is irreversible and the condition is terminal, is within God's permissive will.

Theology does not place importance on life at all costs. While emphasizing that death is not the end, the theologian will be by the physician's side to offer him comfort and counsel when he must make a decision not only to cut off a machine, but also in his decision whether or not he should turn it on in the first place.

Ethical Implications

Ethics is of great concern not only to those in medicine, but also to those in theology. There possibly can be no finer opportunity for the development of ethical ties between the two time-honored disciplines than as they meet in the crisis of death. The theologian respects the physician because he is concerned with people in their most trying times of pain, sickness, suffering and death. There not only is a deep respect for the physician, but anciently, there was a direct association between the fields of medicine and theology. The healer and the spiritual leader were one.

In some cultures of primitive societies today, the medicine man and the spiritual leader are one and the same. This break through the years is not taken to be a hostile one. It was one of necessity. Few men can master successfully more than one discipline. There are few missionary doctors like the late Doctor Dooley of Indo-China. There are few medical doctor-theologians like the late Doctor Albert Schweitzer of Africa. The two disciplines separated because of the vast amount of learning involved in both, not out of animosity.

Even on the mission fields of the world, the missionary doctor is more a healer, while his minister counterpart is more theologian.

Here, at the bedside of the terminally ill, as well as in the relationships they each have to the treatable patient, there can and should be a bond of trust between physician and theologian. While advocating the feeling that a physician should level with his terminally ill patient, this is not to suggest any betrayal of a mutual knowledge of a patient's condition which the minister may have. The reputable minister will not violate a trust he shares. If the physician feels that a given patient ought not to know his true condition, the theologian will not go over the physician's head in informing the patient. In converse, the theologian will not perpetuate a falsehood nor foster a lie, but he certainly is duty-bound not to tell all he knows. The theologian will feel quite comfortable in his role — he may differ in thought and method from the physician, but he will support him in the highest ethical tradition common to both these high callings.

Medical Implications

It is a fact that no one has all the answers to all of the problems all of the time. Physicians are scientists, and it is said that medicine is an exact science. Usually it is, but sometimes it is not.

The introduction of vital organ transplantation has opened debate among members of the medical profession. This is a healthy sign as growth may often come from honest disagreement.

The development of artificial devices, such as pacemakers, respirators, and the discovery of medications for the maintaining of blood pressure, have all served to create a ground for honest disagreement. The traditional definition of death — the cessation of all body functions — has been rejected by an Ad Hoc Committee of the Harvard Medical School whose report was published in the JOURNAL OF THE AMERICAN MEDICAL ASSOCIATION (39). The committee focused attention on the brain and recommended that the patient be declared dead when brain life is shown to have ceased. The committee stated two reasons for the needed redefinition of death:

1. A great burden rests on those patients, their families and even upon hospitals, whose bed space is critical when the patient is allowed to vegetate.
2. There is controversy over the standards established and followed in obtaining organs for transplantation.

The need to update the definition of death will free the patient and his family from needless suffering; the hospital will have the use of the badly needed bed space; the organs will be released for transplant purposes. Doctor Henry K. Beecher, chairman of the committee, has often repeated the statistic that with the average stay of a patient in a hospital set at two weeks, over the course of a year, twenty-six patients who need to be hospitalized cannot be admitted if the bed space is occupied by unsalvageable patients (40).

The problem is extremely complex. The public is uncomfortable in the knowledge that a person's heart is removed while it is still beating or while the patient is still breathing. Yet, it applauds the efforts of the medical team whose skillful techniques in the area of vital human organ transplantation succeed in extending the life of a recipient.

This poses a real dilemma. What is right? How far can one go? The problem has caused some of the more conservative transplant surgeons to wait until all vital signs have ceased before removing the organ to be transplanted, even though the delay may cause the success of the transplanted organ to be less possible. At a conference in Capetown, South Africa, the question arose as to when a heart could be removed from the donor to be used in transplantation, and a difference of opinion among the physicians prevailed. Some of the surgeons present favored the removal of the heart while it was still beating. Others, including Doctor Denton Cooley of Houston, Texas, voted for the heart to cease on its own before it could be removed (41).

There is still another problem — one which has theological, ethical and medical implications. Should any patient have the right to two heart transplants when many others are being denied even one? In following carefully the accounts of those who have received heart transplants, it has been noted that a good number of patients have had two such operations. Consider the case of Gerald Rector: He received his first heart transplant on March 16, 1969, at the University of Michigan Medical Center. He was the one hundred and seventeenth known human heart recipient in the world. On January 16, 1970, he received his second heart. On January 27, 1970, he died. His three chances at life — his original heart plus two transplants — had given this 44-year-old man more chances than the average person will have. William N. Hubbard, Jr., director of the Michigan Medical Center, justified the second heart transplant on the basis that "Rector's body defenses against the foreign heart overwhelmed the suppressive drugs" (42). With two heart transplants, this patient lived just over ten months. Was it worth it? Only he and his family can answer this question. But would there be any cause for guilt when others surely have been denied the first such transplant?

Without referring to the patient above, a new area should be discussed briefly. Consider the case of accident proneness. It is a known fact that certain individuals have poor capacity for coping with hazards encountered in society. Insurance companies often levy higher premiums for such ones classed as accident-prone. The accident-prone person is susceptible to serious illness, traumatic accident and premature death.

However, consider the opposite concept: "life proneness" (43). Could it be that while some are accident-prone and have an unhealthy desire, even if subconsciously, to do damage to their health or person, others may have an unhealthy, exaggerated desire to live? Would the desire to live be so strong that such an individual would go to any limit, financially, physically, medically, in order to prolong his life? If so, would this be considered as an abnormal obsession with the desire not to die? What would the disciplines of medicine and theology say of such a one?

Theology must answer that a person who is so obsessed with the desire to live and not to die, must be ill-prepared for either. Medicine must give its own answer.

NOTES

1. The Holy Bible. Job 14:1-6 RSV.
2. Ibid., Ecclesiastes 3:1-14.
3. Op. Cit., Job 14:14 KJV.
4. Op. Cit., Ecclesiastes 3:11 RSV.
5. Op. Cit., John 10:10 KJV.
6. Ibid., Genesis 2:7.
7. Ibid., Genesis 4:8-12.
8. Webster's New Twentieth Century Dictionary, 2nd ed. New York and Cleveland, World Publishing Company.
9. The Holy Bible. Exodus 20:13 KJV.
10. Ibid., Genesis 1:11.
11. Ibid., Genesis 1:20-21.
12. Ibid., Genesis 1:24.
13. Ibid., Genesis 1:26.
14. Heustis, Albert E.: The two gates of life. In Dilemmas in Faith and the Scientific Manipulation of Life and Death. Council for Health and Welfare Services, United Church of Christ, p. 11.
15. Irion, Paul E.: That life shall have meaning. In Fletcher, Joseph: Morals and Medicine. Princeton, University Press, 1954, p. 34.
16. Hospitals, 43:56, 1969.
17. The Miami Herald. January 29, 1969, p. 22A. Reprinted from The Associated Press and used by permission.
18. Wall Street Journal. Washington D.C. "The Cost of Living," March 10, 1969, p. 1.
19. Webster's Seventh New Collegiate Dictionary. G. & C. Merriam Co., 1970.
20. Barnard, Christiaan: Lecture at Veterans Administration Hospital on January 27, 1969.
21. Hague, James E., Ed.: Editorial notes. Hospitals, 43:47, 1969.
22. Wecht, Cyril H.: Attorney describes current efforts to establish uniform guidelines. Hospitals, 43:54-55, 1969.
23. National Heart Institute: Cardiac Replacement. Ad Hoc Task Force report. Washington, U.S. Government Printing Office, October, 1969, p. 42.

24. Ibid., p. 43.
25. The Miami Herald. Thursday, May 22, 1969, p. 30H. St. Petersburg Times. Permission requested.
26. Op. Cit., Hospitals, p. 56.
27. Ibid.
28. Ibid.
29. Op. Cit., Cardiac Replacement, p. 42.
30. Op. Cit., Hospitals, p. 55.
31. The Holy Bible. II Corinthians 5:1, 6b, 8 KJV.
32. Op. Cit., Webster's New Twentieth Century Dictionary.
33. "Oath of Hippocrates." Copied from one framed in the office of Billy P. Rentz, M.D., Miami, Florida.
34. Herter, Frederic P.: The right to die in dignity. Archives of the Foundation of Thanatology. New York, vol. 1, no. 3, October, 1969, p. 93.
35. Fletcher, Joseph: The right to die. Atlantic Monthly, 221:62-64, 1968, quoted from Theological Studies, vol. 29, no. 4, December, 1968. Archdiocese of Miami. Chancery Library. pp. 704-705. Reprinted with permission.
36. Ibid.
37. Maston, T.B.: Death with dignity. Florida Baptist Witness, August 7, 1969, p. 5.
38. Op. Cit. Oath of Hippocrates.
39. Ethical guidelines for organ transplantation. JAMA, 205:341-342, 1968.
40. Anderson, Fred: Who will decide who is to live? New Republic, April 19, 1969. Reprinted by permission.
41. Ibid.
42. Two-time heart graft patient dies at 44. The Miami News, January 27, 1970.
43. Crane, Diana: Social aspects of the prolongation of life. Social Science Frontiers. New York, Russell Sage Foundation, 1969, pp. 23-24.

Chapter III

MORAL AND ETHICAL CONCERNS: DONOR

THE donor of a vital human organ may either be alive or dead. He may have offered his organ or it may have been offered for him. A donor who is a next of kin may, for example, willingly offer one of his kidneys to save the life of his brother or sister. Such a donation would be a voluntary decision based on sound medical advice that the recipient will die, or at least be chained to a machine the remainder of his life should he not receive a transplanted organ. While there is the normal risk involved in any surgery, it is considered not to be an unusual amount of risk for one to donate one of his two kidneys to sustain the life of another. Currently, it is estimated that the risk is only about 0.5 percent. It is so small a percentage that insurance companies do not change the premium rate for the policy of a donor (1). However, such a donation still qualifies one as a hero — one who is willing to go the extra mile to help someone else.

A person may also become a donor in death. This may be accomplished in two ways:

1. He may elect, prior to his death, to sign a consent willingly expressing his desire to donate his body, or certain parts as may be needed for organ transplantation.
2. He may become a donor in death, when his immediate next of kin voluntarily signs for consent. In either case, whether by his own choosing or by the choice of a next of kin, the one who becomes a donor should have certain basic rights and privileges. These should be protected at all costs by the professional teams involved, by the institution in which the procedure takes place, by the members of the family, and by the public at large.

The Reverend Raymond F. Collins, professor of moral theology, Pope John XXIII, National Seminary, has numbered five rights which he feels are due the donor (2). They are (1) a right to life, (2) a right to die, (3) a right to freedom and personal autonomy, (4) the right to privacy, and (5) the right to bodily respect.

Upon close investigation, one cannot but agree with the Reverend Collins. Mention has already been made about the donor's right to live and a lengthy discussion has already been made above about one's right to die. However, consider the third right that, by common agreement, has been conceded to the donor. A donor *does* have the right, and all concerned should insist on it, to the disposition of his body as he chooses. Previously, if one had indicated a desire to donate his body to medical research, upon his death, his next of kin could reverse his wishes and refuse permission for such disposal of the deceased. But with the coming age of vital human organ transplantation came the Anatomical Gift Act by which a person now has the right to donate all or parts of his body for whatever medical purpose he may choose. The key to this donor's right is in the word "freedom." This is to state that the donor should be left alone without coercion to make his own choice. He may donate or not, and his right should be equally respected. Even in the case of a much-needed organ for transplant purposes, the individual's freedom must not be violated.

The fourth donor right is important for further discussion. Consider the right of the donor for privacy. This has not always been respected, especially in earlier transplant proceedings. Undue publicity is degrading and is an infringement upon the memory of the donor. It is also useless as the published name of the donor will have no real positive value in determining the outcome of the transplant procedure. The families of a donor have suffered untold agonies due to publicity. They have received telephone calls, mail and other expressions, both of concern and of criticism, that have kept alive the memory of the whole proceedings and hindered the healthy working-through of the normal, mature grief-process. Should the donor's family be made to continually suffer such public abuse?

The fifth right is also one deserving of discussion. Consider the right of the donor to be treated with respect in his death: Given, that he has either voluntarily donated his body or parts of it, or some next of kin has donated it for him, he has served humanity rather well in death and is entitled to the proper respect and treatment of his remains by humanity. His body should be shown respect, and when it has served the purpose for which he had intended, it should be given a proper burial with dignity.

THEOLOGICAL

Theology is not merely concerned with the eternal destination of one's soul or spirit once death has occurred. It is a study of God and of man's relationship with Him. Hence, theology is a discipline concerned with man — his life, his relationships with himself and his neighbors — as well as with God. So, theology is vitally concerned with life and how life may be lived more meaningfully and more completely. Theology is concerned with man's total being — both in this world and in the life which surely exists beyond the grave.

Scriptural Evidence

Since no organ transplants were taking place in the time of the writing of the Holy Bible, obviously there are no specific references in Holy Writ. However, one's interpretation of the overall view of God, as seen in progressive revelation, indicates that God is concerned with all of life. In the many instances of healing recorded both in the Old and New Testaments, God is shown to be involved in man's health, his living and death. Jesus was called, or at least made reference to Himself, by use of the physician proverb (3). In another instance, in speaking of repentance, Jesus again noted the value of physicians when He compared the need of the sick for a physician with those who, as sinners, needed a Saviour (4). One of the authors of the four synoptic Gospels was a physician: Luke (5). A view of the mercy and grace of a loving Father — God — would seem to support the fact that He would approve of acceptable methods to contribute to life.

The first human donor very possibly could be named Adam, for if one would take the literal account of the creation of Eve, mother of life, he would find that from a man's organ, a rib, God made woman and gave her life. This he did also while being the first to operate with the use of an anesthetic, "and the Lord God caused a deep sleep to fall upon Adam, and he slept: and He took one of his ribs, and closed up the flesh instead thereof; and the rib, which the Lord God had taken from man, made He a woman, and He brought her unto the man. And Adam said, 'This is now bone of my bones, and flesh of my flesh: she shall be called Woman, because she was taken out of Man' " (6). It is interesting to note that the current surgical term used to describe the completion of an operation is the word "closing." It was used first in reference to God's "closing" of the flesh of Adam. Does medicine borrow from the Holy Bible?

Contemporary Theological Views

There is a decided difference between the various doctrines espoused by people of different faiths. These differences find their places in respect to this new area of human organ transplantation.

Baptist

Baptists are not subject to any particular creed or ruling of hierarchy, but are autonomous in their beliefs and independent in their considerations. They use the Holy Bible as the only rule and guide to their faith. However, the interpretations of the Holy Scriptures differ widely among Baptists. One often wonders if it would not be easier to have a set of rules by which one could develop his own thinking in such matters as how he stands with reference to such areas of thought as organ transplantation. Some churches have it written out and people have but to embrace these rules. Not so with Baptists. The variety among them is because of honest differences. It may be easier, but it would involve less freedom of one's faith.

In the area of organ transplantation, Baptists seem to hold that it is not morally wrong. If the transplant procedure is a standard technique, the physician is free to conduct his practice and is assisted in whatever manner theology can serve him. If the transplant procedure is still in its experimental stage, the physician may wish to consult with individual members of the clergy for their advice and counsel. In general, the Baptist faith, as evidenced in the numerous hospitals which they have built and now support, is very much appreciative of the dedication of the medical profession. The person who may wish to donate his body or parts of it for medical research, or for use in the transplantation of organs, has no doctrinal barrier. The question of artificial insemination and of possible embryo transplants, discussed before, is left to the individual's own thinking and is considered a privilege of one's own conscience.

Roman Catholic

The Roman Catholic Church does have guidelines, and Church dogma may dictate the feelings of the church regarding many aspects of organ transplantation and donation. In the area of artificial insemination, the church is opposed and flatly denies such permission. The Catholic Church is not opposed to the transplanting of one's own tissue or organs either during the life of the donor or at his death. The integrity of the donor must always remain undamaged. Any attempt to transplant sex glands is considered immoral.

Episcopalian

The Episcopal Church has not issued a formal statement regarding the use of artificial insemination, but leaders of the church in general have taken the individual position that it would be morally acceptable as a responsible procreative aim. Expanding on the subject, the Church of England ruled that the donor must be the husband of the recipient. As to organ transplantation, the church has found nothing spiritually offensive and believes it to be of use to the plan of God's creation.

Liberal Judaism

The Central Conference of American Rabbis has denounced the

use of any measure intended to hasten death. However, the Conference also has agreed that there is no virtue in prolonging life as a mere biological process. While recognizing the right of a patient to die, the Conference opposes euthanasia.

As to the use of artificial insemination, the Conference has agreed that it is not morally wrong. The rabbis qualify their belief by stating that the identity of the donor should be concealed from the recipient, and that her spouse and their identity should be unknown to the donor.

In the area of organ transplantation, the conference has authorized the removal of eyes from a cadaver if it is possible to restore the sight to one who is living. This includes the removal of any other organ from a deceased person for use in transplantation. The permission for organ donation is restricted to one who is dead. One who is living may not donate an organ to another living person no matter how close the relationship, as this would be interpreted as an act of mutiliation to the living donor and is strongly forbidden in Jewish law.

Orthodox Judaism

Artificial insemination is forbidden on the grounds that it is contrary to God's Eternal Law and also to nature. The "right to die" is viewed as actually the practice of euthanasia and is regarded as outright murder. In the area of organ transplantation, if it is necessary for the saving of life, the decision is left to the discretion of the individual rabbi. Jewish Law requires that any organ of the human body must be given proper burial and in the case of the recipient's death, the donor's organ would then have to be given ritual burial (7).

LEGAL

A questionnaire was sent to three hundred physicians. The response from them indicated that a primary concern of the medical profession was in protecting themselves against possible legal action in the area of organ transplantation. They were asked the question, "What do you think is the major moral or ethical problem as it involves the donor of a major organ?" Of the eighty-eight who responded, forty-nine listed as their answer, the determination of time of clinical death. Thirty-seven checked the answer, gaining family's consent for removal of organs. Twenty-two listed as their answer, legal restrictions or possibility of legal action against the physician. In short, these physicians are concerned about the legal aspects involving organ transplantation and are especially concerned with the donor.

The surgeon who performed the first liver transplant in West Germany has been sued for $3,000 by the donor's relatives. They claim that Doctor Alfred Guetgemann, head of the Surgical Unit in Bonn's University Clinic, violated personal rights by not seeking their consent for the transplanted organ (8). The laws of West Germany do not object to surgical transplants as long as next of kin have granted permission. The case is expected to set a precedent which will give some moral and legal guidelines to help surgeons face the decisions involved in transplantation of human organs.

In dealing further with the moral and ethical concerns involving the donor, one is faced with at least two questions:

1. How does one go about the matter of donating his major organs for transplantation?
2. How can he be sure his desires to do so will be carried out after his death?

John Pusey, of the law firm of Vorachen, Cation, Lawless, Trager, and Slevin, of Peoria, Illinois, has presented a paper in which he explores the various legal implications involved in organ transplants, and particularly, those having to do with the heart (9). The problem, as he sees it, involves the legal machinery needed to allow one to become a donor if he so chooses.

"The Last Will and Testament, that time-honored and safe way of disposing of one's property to whom one wishes, and in the manner in which he wishes . . . in its traditional form is out," he states. The heart must be removed from the donor immediately after his death and transplanted into the body of the recipient immediately. However, the will cannot take effect until after it has been probated, and the time span between the death of the one desiring to so will his heart, and the actual probating of the will, would be so great as to rule out any possible use of the surgical team.

Then, as Pusey continues, "What about the person's donating his heart by making it known during his lifetime, or during his last illness, that he wishes to be a heart donor? Fine — but there is a possible difficulty here, too. The heart cannot be removed until after "death," and once a person is dead, it is then up to his next of kin what is to be done with the body. If the next of kin decides that the heart of the deceased may not be taken, then it simply cannot be taken. A living declaration of one's intention to be a heart donor, therefore, is less than foolproof" (10).

Uniform Anatomical Gift Act

The difficulties pointed out by Pusey have served to bring into being the Uniform Anatomical Gift Act. This act was adopted by the National Conference of Commissioners on Uniform State Laws in July, 1968, and was also approved by the American Bar Association in August, 1968. Later, in March, 1969, the House of Delegates of the American Medical Association recommended the adoption of the act, and as of August 20, 1969, the following thirty-seven states had adopted it (11):

Alabama	Louisiana	Ohio
Arkansas	Maine	Oklahoma
California	Maryland	Oregon
Colorado	Michigan	South Carolina
Connecticut	Minnesota	South Dakota
Florida	Missouri	Tennessee
Georgia	Montana	Texas
Hawaii	Nevada	Utah
Idaho	New Jersey	Vermont
Illinois	New Mexico	Washington
Indiana	North Carolina	Wisconsin
Iowa	North Dakota	Wyoming
Kansas		

It is almost a surety that the other states have, or will adopt the act.

The Attorneys General to whom questionnaires were sent have been most responsive, sending personal letters and copies of legislation passed or pending in their respective states. The author is appreciative to each of them for their cooperation. Since this Uniform Anatomical Gift Act is the ultimate law, as it pertains to the whole area of human organ transplantation, it is quoted in its entirety. The author expresses deep appreciation to the National Conference of Commissioners on Uniform State Laws for permission to publish this act (12).

SECTION I (DEFINITIONS)

(a) "Bank or storage facility" means a facility licensed, accredited or approved under the laws of any state for storage of human bodies or parts thereof.

(b) "Decedent" means a deceased individual and includes a stillborn infant or fetus.

(c) "Donor" means an individual who makes a gift of all or part of his body.

(d) "Hospital" means a hospital licensed, accredited or approved under the laws of any state and includes a hospital operated by the United States government, a state or a subdivision thereof, although not required to be licensed under state laws.

(e) "Part" includes organs, tissues, eyes, bones, arteries, blood, other fluids and other portions of a human body, and "part" includes "parts."

(f) "Person" means an individual, corporation, government or governmental subdivision or agency, business trust, estate, trust, partnership or association or any other legal entity.

(g) "Physician" or "surgeon" means a physician or surgeon licensed or authorized to practice under the laws of any state.

(h) "State" includes any state, district, commonwealth, territory, insular possession, and any other area subject to the legislative authority of the United States of America.

SECTION 2 (PERSONS WHO MAY EXECUTE AN ANATOMICAL GIFT)

(a) Any individual of sound mind and eighteen years of age or more may give all or any part of his body for any purposes specified in Section 3, the gift to take effect upon death.

(b) Any of the following persons, in order of priority stated, when persons in prior classes or not available at the time of death, and in the absence of actual notice of contrary indications by the decedent, or actual notice of opposition by a member of the same or a prior class, may give all or any part of the decedent's body for any purposes specified in Section 3.

(1) the spouse,

(2) an adult son or daughter,

(3) either parent,

(4) an adult brother or sister,

(5) a guardian of the person of the decedent at the time of his death,

(6) any other person authorized or under obligation to dispose of the body.

(c) If the donee has actual notice of contrary indications by the decedent, or that a gift by a member of a class is opposed by a member of the same or a prior class, the donee shall not accept the gift. The persons authorized by subsection (b) may make the gift after death or immediately before death.

(d) A gift of all or part of a body authorizes any examination necessary to assure medical acceptability of the gift for the purposes intended.

(e) The rights of the donee created by the gift are paramount to the right of others except as provided by Section 7(d).

SECTION 3 (PERSONS WHO MAY BECOME DONEES, AND PURPOSES FOR WHICH ANATOMICAL GIFTS MAY BE MADE)

The following persons may become donees of gifts of bodies or parts thereof for the purposes stated:

(1) any hospital, surgeon, or physician, for medical or dental education, research, advancement of medical or dental science, therapy or transplantation; or

(2) any accredited medical or dental school, college or university for education, research, advancement of medical or dental science or therapy; or

(3) any bank or storage facility for medical or dental education, research, advancement of medical or dental science, therapy or transplantation; or

(4) any specified individual for therapy or transplantation needed by him.

SECTION 4 (MANNER OF EXECUTING ANATOMICAL GIFTS)

(a) A gift of all or part of the body under Section 2(a) may be made by will. The gift becomes effective upon the death of the testator without waiting for probate. If the will is not probated, or if it is declared invalid for testamentary purposes, the gift, to the extent that it has been acted upon in good faith, is nevertheless valid and effective.

(b) A gift of all or part of the body under Section 2(a) may also be made by document other than a will. The gift becomes effective upon the death of the donor. The document, which may be a card designed to be carried on the person, must be signed by the donor, in the presence of two witnesses who must sign the document in his presence. If the donor cannot sign, the document may be signed for him at his direction and in his presence, and in the presence of two witnesses who must sign the document in his presence. Delivery of the document of gift during the donor's lifetime is not necessary to make the gift valid.

(c) The gift may be made to a specified donee or without specifying a donee. If the latter, the gift may be accepted by the attending physician as donee upon or following death. If the gift is made to a specified donee who is not available at the time and place of death, the attending physician upon or following death, in the absence of any expressed indication that the donor desired otherwise, may accept the gift as donee. The physician who becomes a donee under this subsection shall not participate in the procedures for removing or transplanting a part.

(d) Notwithstanding Section 7(b), the donor may designate in his will, card or other document of gift the surgeon or physician to carry out the appropriate procedures. In the absence of a designation, or if the designee is not available, the donee or other person authorized to accept the gift may employ or authorize any surgeon or physician for the purpose.

(e) Any gift by a person designated in Section 2(b) shall be made a document signed by him, or made by his telegraphic, recorded telephonic or other recorded message.

SECTION 5 (DELIVERY OF DOCUMENT OF GIFT)

If the gift is made by the donor to a specified donee, the will, card, or other document, or an executed copy thereof, may be delivered to the donee to expedite the appropriate procedures immediately after death, but delivery is not necessary to the validity of the gift. The will, card or other document, or an executed copy thereof, may be deposited in any hospital, bank or storage facility or registry office that accepts them for safekeeping or for facilitation of procedures after death. On request of any interested party upon or after the donor's death, the person in possession shall produce the document for examination.

SECTION 6 (AMENDMENT OR REVOCATION OF THE GIFT)

(a) If the will, card or other document or executed copy thereof has been delivered to a specified donee, the donor may amend or revoke the gift by:
   (1) the execution and delivery to the donee of a signed statement, or
   (2) an oral statement made in the presence of two persons and communicated to the donee, or
   (3) a statement during a terminal illness or injury addressed to an attending physician and communicated to the donee, or
   (4) a signed card or document found on his person or in his effects.
(b) Any document of gift which has not been delivered to the donee may be revoked by the donor in the manner set out in subsection (a) or by destruction, cancellation, or mutilation of the document and all executed copies thereof.
(c) Any gift made by a will may also be amended or revoked in the manner provided for amendment or revocation of wills, or as provided in subsection (a).

SECTION 7 (RIGHTS AND DUTIES OF DEATH)

(a) The donee may accept or reject the gift. If the donee accepts a gift of the entire body, he may, subject to the terms of the gift, authorize embalming and the use of the body in funeral services. If the gift is a part of the body, the donee, upon the death of the donor and prior to embalming, shall cause the part to be removed without unnecessary mutilation. After removal of the part, custody of the remainder of the body rests in the surviving spouse, next of kin or other person under obligation to dispose of the body.
(b) The time of death shall be determined by a physician who attends the donor at his death, or, if none, the physician who certifies the death. This physician shall not participate in the procedures for removing or transplanting a part.
(c) A person who acts in good faith in accord with the terms of this act, or under the anatomical gift laws of another state (or a foreign country) is not liable for damages in any civil action or subject to prosecution in any criminal proceeding for his act.
(d) The provisions of this act are subject to the laws of this state prescribing powers and duties with respect to autopsies.

SECTION 8 (UNIFORMITY OF INTERPRETATION)

This act shall be so construed as to effectuate its general purpose to make uniform the law of those states which enact it.

SECTION 9 (SHORT TITLE)

This act may be cited as the Uniform Anatomical Gift Act.

Signed Consent by Next of Kin

Already, some discussion has been opened to the important matter concerning the signed consent when transplantation of human organs is contemplated. The Uniform Anatomical Gift Act reproduced in full above has indicated how this may be done. The following is a copy used by the Miami Heart Institute and the author expresses his appreciation for permission to reproduce it in its entirety (13).

Date: _____

1. I the undersigned, (_____)
   (Donor)

   or the next of kin of (_____)
   (Insert name of Donor)

   hereby give consent for the removal of the following tissue or organs

   _____ from _____
   (Insert name of Donor)

   for donation to _____ .
   (Insert name of Recipient)

2. The undersigned hereby waives for myself or my heirs any claim or

   demand which I may have against the Miami Heart Institute, Inc., the

   surgeons, doctors, nurses, or other agents, servants and employees of the

   hospital who participate in the removal of tissue or organs from the donor

   for transplanting.

Witnesses:

_____   _____ (Seal)
                                                (Donor)
_____

AS TO DONOR

_____   _____ (Seal)
                                                (Next of kin)
_____

AS TO NEXT OF KIN

Complications Involving Death of Donor from Criminal Actions

There are many entanglements connected with human organ transplantation. Most of these shall be legally dealt with to the satisfaction of all concerned by the enactment of laws such as are listed in detail above. But what of the involvements concerning the complications resulting from transplanting of human organs taken from one who has been the victim of criminal attack? Who is guilty of a death — the one who assaulted the person, thus inflicting severe and critical injuries, or the surgeon who may have removed a beating heart from the victim?

Again, the definition of the time of death is of utmost importance. This has been discussed at length before. But consider this case which is reportedly a true fact (14):

A 62-year-old man lay dying of advanced cardiac disease in Saint Luke's Episcopal Hospital in Houston. His surgeon, the noted Doctor Denton Cooley, had recommended a heart transplant and his patient had consented. There was no donor. At nearby Methodist Hospital in Houston, surgeons had given up hope of saving a thirty-six-year-old man who had been beaten and battered by an assailant. With his wife's consent the dying man was transferred to Saint Luke's.

The medical examiner expressed doubts as to the legality for the anticipated transplant. The reason for the medical examiner's doubts was that the young man was still alive in the sense that his heart and lungs were functioning via artificial respirators. But the EEG showed that brain function had stopped completely and the attending physician accordingly pronounced the man dead. Again, the medical examiner was not so sure. His argument amounted to this: Traditionally, death had always been defined as that moment when the heartbeat and breathing stopped. Here, even though the EEG showed that there was absolutely no brain function, the heart and lungs were nonetheless functioning even if by means of the artificial respirators. Since state law would require an autopsy under the circumstances, the medical examiner was afraid that technically the cause of death, were the man's heart to be removed from his body, would not be the massive brain damage which he had suffered as a result of the criminal assault, but the actual removal of the heart itself.

When it finally became apparent that death, even in the traditional sense, was imminent, the medical examiner promised not to file charges against Doctor Cooley for interfering with the autopsy (but warned of the possibility of other legal entanglements); Doctor Cooley performed the heart transplant.

Now, one may see the extent of the possible legal difficulties. What would be the outcome when the donor's accused attacker was brought to trial? Could the defense counsel argue that death had not occurred at the time the patient was pronounced dead, but later when the heart, still beating, was removed? Also, if the traditional view of death — the cessation of heartbeat and breathing — is carried to its logical conclusion, it may be argued by the defense that, since the victim's heart never really stopped beating, and was still beating in the body of another, the victim of the assault had never really expired. There would be no case for murder against the assailant.

Some years ago, an Englishman named John David Potter was involved in a fight. He was rushed to the Newcastle General Hospital, critically injured with evident brain damage. After fourteen hours, his breathing stopped. Under such circumstances, he would have been pronounced dead, but a kidney was needed for transplantation and *he* was to be the donor. He was placed on a respirator and kept breathing artificially. His heartbeat and circulation began again and his kidney was being preserved pending transplant proceedings. For the next twenty-four hours, Potter's vital signs were kept going by the use of artificial means. His wife gave permission for a kidney to be removed to be used in transplantation in another patient. This done, the attending physician ordered the respirator to be turned off. Potter's breathing ceased — his heart stopped.

At the inquest, the central question was, "When and from what cause did Potter die?" The coroner felt that the kidney had been taken before death. A hospital physician partly agreed in that Potter was MEDICALLY dead when he first stopped breathing. He was not LEGALLY dead until a day later when the machine was turned off. A government pathologist and a consulting neuro-surgeon decided that brain damage was the cause of Potter's death and that he was dead before the kidney was removed. The jury ruled that the removal of the kidney had nothing to do with the man's death and reached a verdict of manslaughter against the assailant who had injured Potter (15).

The definition of death must be changed and the criteria discussed earlier should be that which constitutes clinical death.

The transplantation of human organs has both necessitated and demanded this change.

MEDICAL

In discussing the theological and legal concerns as they apply to the donor, some of the medical aspects were touched upon. However, to expand further without unnecessary repetition may be of interest.

Rules Regulating Attending Physicians

The physicians that may be involved in a case of transplantation are related in two ways: some are in attendance upon the donor, and some are in attendance upon the prospective recipient. Already, it has been pointed out that physicians involved in the pronouncement of death of a donor may not be involved in the transplantation of a vital human organ to a proposed recipient. The reasons are obvious: there must be no conflict of interest, and no attempt at allowing the end to justify the means. Thus, the physician of the donor is pledged by his oath and by the ethics of his profession to take the best possible care of his patient, to do no harm, to ease suffering and give his best for the patient's benefits. The physician who cares for the prospective recipient is equally pledged to his patient.

Thus, the two are not in competition, but rather, in agreement with the aims of each other. One's desire to save the patient who has a greater chance at living must never violate the ethics of the other whose patient deserves the best medical care available.

Responsibilities of Physician to Donor

As discussed earlier, the donor's physician must not do harm, nor withhold what may actually help the would-be donor to have a meaningful life. He will attend the prospective donor with his very best skill and will make use of his knowledge in order to bring wholeness to his patient. He is not ethically nor morally bound to perpetuate a vegetable. When it is clear to the physician that the donor is clinically dead, based on the criteria above, he may assume the responsibility to turn off the machine, discontinue the other stimulants, and admit that death is not an enemy that has been conquered. Death is a reality and this side of eternity has never been conquered.

The Pronouncement of Death

The pronouncement of death has always and should ever be the responsibility of the medical doctor. Though there are different classifications of death (i.e., legal, spiritual and medical), it is the peculiar duty of the physician to determine the time of death of the person. The physician will continue to assume this responsibility whether or not there is a change definitely in the criteria to determine death. It is this writer's opinion that the medical profession will continue to serve the needs of mankind and will proceed with the adaptation to any new criteria that is found to be ethically and professionally sound.

Criteria for Judgment As To Time Of Death

The opinion of the attending physician will prevail, as in the past, in use of criteria for determining the time of death. When no plans are evident for transplantation of human organs, the physician may still use the normal "old-fashioned" way of determining death. He will check the vital signs — the lack of blood pressure, the cessation of breathing, the stoppage of the heartbeat, the fixed and dilated pupil — and on this basis pronounce the time of death. But when a possible transplantation of a vital human organ is involved, he will avail himself of all the equipment necessary to determine the "brain death," up to and including the consultation from at least two other physicians. These shall, of course, have no immediate interest nor participation in the transplant team.

Use of Mechanical Devices to Determine Death

The use of the EEG and the interpretation of its results must be certified by those who are competent in the use of such equipment. Every feasible manner in which competent physicians may check to determine death should be employed before any attempts to remove vital organs are initiated.

With these assurances which competent, ethical physicians are anxious to share, there seems to be no good reason why the terminally ill patient or his next of kin would not be willing to give consent for use of vital organs that may save the life, or eyesight of some other person. Doctor Christiaan Barnard said it well: "Is it not immoral to bury a heart when we have the ability to save a life?"

NOTES

1. Hospitals, p. 50, November 1, 1969.
2. Collins, Reverend Raymond F.: Heart Transplants: Ethical Considerations. A pamphlet. pp. 59-61. From Catholic Lawyer, Winter, 1969.
3. The Holy Bible. Luke 4:23-24 KJV.
4. Ibid., Mark 2:17.
5. Ibid., Colossians 4:14.
6. Ibid., Genesis 2:21-23.
7. For further study, consult: The Faith of Your Patients: A Handbook on Religious Attitudes Toward Medical Practices. Pamphlet compiled by the Committee on Medicine and Religion of the Los Angeles County Medical Association.
8. The Miami News. September 25, 1969. p. 9C.
9. Pusey, John: The legal implications of heart transplants. Peoria, Illinois. Unpublished material. Used by permission.
10. Ibid., John Pusey.
11. National Heart Institute: Cardiac Replacement, Washington, U.S. Government Printing Office, October, 1969, Appendix 8, p. 90.
12. National Conference of Commissioners on Uniform State Laws, Chicago, July 30, 1968.
13. Consent of donor or next of kin for removal after death of tissue or organs for transplanting. Miami Heart Institute, Inc., Miami Beach, Florida, Robert Summers, administrator.
14. Op. Cit., John Pusey: The legal implications of heart transplants. Quoted from Newsweek, May 20, 1968. Used by permission.
15. Stevens, Leonard A.: When is death? The Reader's Digest. May, 1969, pp. 225-226.

Chapter IV

MORAL AND ETHICAL CONCERNS: RECIPIENT

T HE normal thing for a person is to want to live. It is abnormal to want to die. It is morally wrong for one to take human life, either his own or another's. Under certain circumstances, the normal may become abnormal, and the abnormal may become normal. For instance, the normal thing is for one to want to live, to take all due precautions to sustain his life. Yet, under the circumstances of terminal illness when pain is agonizing and life is a burden, this person may really desire to slip away quietly in death. This would not be an abnormal desire. To fight to live at the cost of constant pain and agony, when life itself is an unbearable experience, may then become abnormal. Thus, the words "normal" and "abnormal" must be weighed with attention given to the circumstances in which they are used.

God placed within the human personality a strong desire for life and self-preservation. This drive is good. It is of extreme value to the healing professions and may determine the outcome of a given procedure. It is called "the will to live." One who has a healthy, strong will to live may indeed survive when another in like circumstance may die because of a lack of a strong and determined will to live. It is God-given; it is good. But are there instances when one's will to live becomes more of an obsession? Can one reach the point in life when he fights against the very thought of dying until his life is eaten up by the morbid preoccupation with death? Is this normal? Is it morally right?

Already, in considering the case of Doctor Phillip Blaiberg, the longest living heart recipient, reference was made to Doctor Christiaan Barnard's question to the widow when the famed heart patient died. Doctor Barnard had asked her, "Was it really worth it?" The fact that Doctor Barnard had to ask the question seems to indicate a measure of doubt in his own mind. He was reassured when Mrs. Blaiberg replied, "Yes, you know it was worth it."

In considering the moral and ethical concerns involving the recipient, one must leave to each one individually, the question, "Was it really worth it?" After all, only those patients and their families are really qualified to answer.

Nevertheless, one must explore some of the various ramifications surrounding the recipient.

THEOLOGICAL

When God breathed into man's nostrils the breath of life, man became a living soul (1). With this life, man became a responsible being. He accepted life. He embraced life. He should love life, but he should also use a part of his life to prepare for his death. So, man was born to live and also to die. The fact that man can accept in a mature manner the inevitability of death does not mean he does not love life, but rather, that in accepting the reality of death, he learns how to live. So, the one who knows how to live and enjoy life, with all that it entails, knows that death is unavoidable and prepares for its coming. Having prepared for its coming, he then ceases to be preoccupied with it and begins to live.

A man does not buy life insurance merely because he is morbidly preoccupied with death. He buys it for protection of his loved ones so that, in the event of his death, they may be cared for. Having adequately made necessary provisions for his death, he is then able to pursue life more freely.

The doctrine of death seems to be just here applicable. One prepares in this life for his approaching death. He makes spiritual preparation, embraces good sound religion, acknowledges God as his Savior, and then turns to the business of living — contributing to, as well as receiving from, life.

Limitations as to Sustaining Life

Already discussed at length, are limits that should be set on how far one should go in prolonging life and averting death. However, in the case of the recipient of a vital human organ, it is a fact that each has already been confronted with the inevitability of death. One of the requirements for a recipient is to have a condition that is irreversible and not subject to any other method of treatment. In this aspect, each recipient of a vital human organ transplant may be said to be in the position of "cheating death," or of taking unusual and drastic methods to avert death. In the case of kidney transplantation, the rate of success has been so improved as to all but extinguish the "unusual or drastic" risks involved. In short, it has become an acceptable method of treating the patient who would die but for this surgery. Will this success later be inclusive of heart, lung and liver transplants? Medical science is optimistic and hard at work to make it so.

Preparation for Death

The medical profession looks to theologians of all faiths to help educate the public in certain matters of medical practice, obtaining of autopsies, helping to gain tolerance and understanding in matters concerning transplantation of human organs, and in many other ways. Theologians gladly share in dialogue with physicians and are willing to give assistance in every possible way. The reciprocal is welcomed and, in most cases, is evidenced.

In the matter of preparing one for death, the theologian must be welcomed as a vital member of the team. While the patient is the responsibility of the attending physician in charge, it is unthinkable that any reputable member of the medical profession would seek to prevent the preparation of his patient for death. In this, theologians of every faith stand united. The reputable theologian will call upon his training, skill, experience and love of mankind to act discreetly in every case. He will not violate trusted faith invested in him by divulging information to which he may have access. Yet, he must be allowed the privilege of preparing the dying to face death realistically and with some degree of maturity. He looks to medical science for understanding and cooperation and is entitled to their respect and the freedom necessary to perform his function.

Last Rites

For want of a better phrase, this concept of last rites has stuck.

There are better terms and some are now being used. A better term is "spiritual preparation" or "sacrament to the dying" or "anointing of the ill" or simply, "pastoral care of the sick." In each case, the theologian must have freedom to minister to the needs of the patient.

In the case of a proposed recipient of a vital organ transplant, the importance of spiritual preparation is vital. The physician has already informed the patient of his terminal condition. He has discussed the risks involved in transplantation. The patient has signed consent for the surgery. He knows the risks and his chances. He then should be given opportunity for pastoral care from the hospital chaplain or from his own minister, priest or rabbi.

Contrary to general thought, the patient need not necessarily feel that pastoral care is an evidence that he is going to die. The skilled theologian will not communicate this feeling at all. The reverse is most often true. Having had the opportunity for pastoral care and the dialogue that allows for free expression of one's feelings, the patient may feel a release that can now turn his thoughts and energies to the task of getting well.

Confessional

In all faiths, there is a channel for confession. This is formally spelled out in some such as in the Roman Catholic Church, which includes the confessional as one of the sacraments. But whether formalized or less structured, there is a place in all faiths for one to confess his sins and mistakes in life. This is called "catharsis" in the jargon of psychiatry and "ventilation" in the language of the counselor, but in reality, they are the same — confession, catharsis and ventilation — and serve the same purpose. The patient must have the opportunity for this self-searching and soul-cleansing. This is especially true in regards to the proposed recipient of a major organ transplant. He may have guilt feelings over the cost of the procedure. He may have ambivalent feelings as to whether the risks, anxieties, and strains on his loved ones really warrant the operation at all.

In any case, he must be given an opportunity to "talk it out" with his spiritual advisor — minister, priest, rabbi or hospital chaplain. In considering all the other areas regarding the recipient, it would be most unwise to overlook this important aspect. Here again, the reputable theologian of whatever faith will neither coerce nor lead the patient. He will merely create the environment that will allow the patient to discuss his own feelings. This period of confession should not be looked upon by the medical profession in any sense as the patient's admission of defeat, threatened loss of a will to live, or that the patient may be talked out of going through with the procedure. The reputable clergyman will not attempt to make such decisions for his parishioner. If there is a case in which the person's particular faith has teachings against any such transplant proceedings, then the patient either would not have become a candidate as a recipient, or his willingness would clearly indicate that in this specific area, he does not share the teachings of his faith.

Reputable physicians will not attempt to block off the clergy from their role any more than the clergy would seek to stop the physician from the free practice of his profession.

Spiritual Support

While the members of the clergy will not seek to make the decisions for their parishioners in the matter of transplantation of vital organs, they will be present to give spiritual support when the decisions are made to either proceed or desist in further attempts to sustain life.

Whatever the individual clergyman may personally feel about the worth of organ transplantation, it will in no way influence his spiritual concern for, and pastoral care of, the patient. The patient has a right to be a recipient if he so chooses, and the spiritual advisor will offer his support in the decision that the patient has freely made.

LEGAL

There are various forms of consent which must be signed. The patient, or as in the case of a minor or one who is otherwise incapable, his legally authorized representative must sign, indicating one's desire to be a recipient and giving certification of the knowledge of the risks and dangers involved. The following is a copy of the form used by the Miami Heart Institute of Miami Beach, Florida (2):

CONSENT TO OPERATION FOR TRANSPLANTING
OF HUMAN ORGANS

Date: _____

_____
(Recipient)

1. I hereby request and authorize Doctor _____ and

such other surgeons and physicians as he may designate to perform

upon _____ in the Miami Heart Institute, Miami
      (Name of Patient)
Beach, Florida, the following operation _____

and to perform any other procedure that his judgment may indicate

during the operation.

2. I am informed that the above operation will require the removal of a

diseased or injured _____ and a transplanting of
      (Insert Name of Organ)
_____ and that the organ to be used will be supplied
(Insert Name of Organ)
by _____

(Insert Name of Donor or Organ Bank)

3. I understand the procedure proposed, its potential benefits and its possible

adverse affect. I have further been informed of my present condition as it

exists and with what I might expect if no surgery is performed. I further

understand that I am living in a most precarious life and that the

traditional methods of treating the condition have been exhausted and if I undergo the transplant I may expire if it fails. I further understand that if the transplantation is only partially successful I may live but life may be worse than it has been because of lack of knowledge and ability to overcome the rejection process. The risks involved in such an undertaking have been fully explained to me. No warranty has been made by anyone as to the results that may be obtained.

4. I understand that the operating surgeon will be occupied solely with the surgery and that the administration of the anaesthetic (s) is an independent function and will be in charge of Doctor _____ , or others as he may designate, whom I authorize to administer such anaesthetic (s) as he may deem advisable.

5. I do hereby waive for myself or my heirs any claim or demand in which I may have of any nature, kind or description against the Miami Heart Institute, Inc., or any of the surgeons, doctors, nurses, or other agents, servants and employees of the hospital who participate in the operation for the transplanting of the human organ, and I do specifically assume any and all responsibility for the operation and the same is done at my request and for my benefit.

Witnesses:

_____   _____ (Seal)

(Recipient)

_____

If the recipient is a minor, or is under any disability, then his or her legally

authorized representative.

_____ (Seal)
(Representative Capacity)

Witnesses:

_____

_____

_____ (Seal)
(Representative Capacity)

_____

_____

Agreement of Financial Involvements

Whatever other considerations may be involved in the decisions to be made by a prospective recipient, the economic one is of importance and must be faced. The plain, simple fact is that human organ transplantation is expensive!

Consider the case of Herbert Minchew. He was given a kidney transplant at the Miami Heart Institute on Friday, April 25, 1969. According to the hospital's administrator, "the bill would be about $26,000 . . . he did not know where Minchew would get the money" (3). A source close to the Minchew family indicated they had spent all they had keeping him alive. He had been receiving hemodialysis treatments for about three years, on a kidney machine which had been purchased by funds donated by the community. The administrator of the Heart Institute in which the operation was performed was quoted as saying, "Financial arrangements haven't been worked out. But I would guess — if the patient has insurance — we will collect that and the hospital will pick up the remaining cost" (4).

This is good and noble, but how many such transplants can a hospital pay for before either going into bankruptcy or being endowed by funds from private or governmental agencies? Now again comes the question, "How can one put a price tag on life?" But there are costs and someone must pay — the patient, his family, his community, the government, the taxpayers — someone must assume the financial burden. The recipient should not have to voice, as his first response upon waking up from surgery, concern over his soaring medical bills. A heart recipient who received his new heart from the same donor of the kidney given to patient Minchew is reported to have been "talking with his family . . . and also wondering how to pay his medical bills" (5).

Should not these financial matters be settled before the procedure? Should not an understanding be reached between the recipient and his family with the physicians and with the hospital involved as to the cost, method of payment, discounts and write-offs?

The sad consequence is that bills may be so extremely high that the recipient, should he live, will be hopelessly debt-bound the remainder of his "new life." Very often, too, his ability to work and earn the money necessary to meet his financial obligations will either be greatly reduced, or cut off altogether.

The possible result, unless some form of planned assistance from private sources or government subsidies is available, may be that those who can afford to pay may live while those who cannot afford to pay may die. Dare we allow the total program of organ transplantation to be reduced to this set of cold, hard facts?

The question was put to physicians and surgeons throughout the nation and in some foreign countries, "Do you believe government subsidy or outright gifts will be necessary to insure the average person an equal chance for a major organ transplant?" The question was answered overwhelmingly in the affirmative, forty-eight to fourteen. The question then was asked, "Are you in favor of such gifts or subsidy?" Again the response was conclusive. They answered in the affirmative, forty to ten.

Is it morally right to save a person for a lifetime of hopeless indebtedness? Can society expect physicians to continually donate their services in the care of a recipient for a major transplant procedure? Can hospitals and major medical centers justify the writing-off of these expensive charges, thus, in reality, charging other inpatients higher costs to offset losses? Can tax-supported institutions justify the increases in taxation necessary to pay for these huge bills?

The questions are real. They are factual. They seem rather coldly put, but denial of reality never solves problems that are real. One does not expect to find solutions unless he is willing to face the problems.

Understanding Between Next of Kin

At no time is there greater need for understanding and communication between a critically ill patient and his family than in the case of a prospective transplant recipient. There should be no barriers, real or imaginary, set up. Open and frank discussion not only is expected, but should be insisted upon. Actually, and in a real sense, the decision to become a recipient is a multiple one — involving the recommendation of the physicians based upon their laboratory findings, the patient's willingness and the family's acceptance. All should be in agreement and thoroughly understand what is involved. If the family is large and somewhat scattered, complete unanimity may be needless and impossible, but the basic members should agree.

Potential Dangers of Black Market

"There is honor even among thieves," so it has been said. But where one's life is involved, could there be a possible black market that would spring up and cast its shadow over the whole area of human organ transplantation? In short, could a "ne're-do-well" seize upon a one chance-in-a-lifetime to duck out of life and leave his family with a $50,000 nest egg? Could he bargain with a wealthy heart patient to sell his heart for a sum to be placed in escrow for his family after he jumps from a bridge?

There are so many loose ends to the whole question (i.e., tissue-matching, time and place of death, selection of proper recipient) as to perhaps prevent such a lucrative business from developing. But then, some states, seemingly anticipating such possible underhanded practices, are passing laws forbidding a recipient from paying for the gift, and heirs and next of kin cannot revoke the gift (6).

MEDICAL

There are certain criteria which must be met for one to become a recipient of a vital human organ transplant. Since the number of recipients is larger than the number of donors, the problem of selection becomes not only a medical concern, but also, one of morality.

Methods of Selection

Physicians have generally taken the position that the paramount consideration in selection of a recipient should be biomedical. Tissue-typing is a prime factor in the selection of a recipient and proper consideration must be given if any degree of success is to be anticipated. There are some physicians who would make this the final criteria. In any case, before any patient can be considered for an organ transplant, he must have these three basic criteria:

1. He must have irreversible, incurable disease.

2. He must have failed to respond to any and all other methods of treatment for the disease.

3. He must have reached a point in which the disease has been diagnosed as terminal and he must be in the terminal stages.

This qualifies the patient as an eligible recipient and he can then be placed in a state of readiness. He may be removed to a hospital or medical center where he undergoes a series of testing to determine his particular biomedical makeup. He may be placed in a "stand-by" condition for an indeterminate time until a dying person has sufficient tissue-matching to risk a transplant operation.

But the question must come: "How is the selection made when more than one patient, standing by, has sufficient tissue-matching to warrant a transplant attempt?" In this case, there must be a selection based upon criteria other than the biomedical. Some have suggested, in addition to the physician's use of tissue-typing, the setting up of committees to help select a patient as to his worth toward society. Again, some medical centers have established psychiatric screening for potential recipients.

Tissue Typing

The main cause of transplant failures is in the problem of rejection. As seen before, this was found to be by far the main cause for the death of those who had received heart transplants. Although use of immunosuppressive drugs helps combat the problems of rejection, the more closely the tissue-typing, the better the chances are for survival. Physicians will check the potential recipient's blood type. They will also begin a series of laboratory procedures designed to type the tissues of the recipient, later to be cross-matched with a donor. The availability of the services of microbiologists and biochemists are of absolute necessity for the requirements of a medical center or hospital engaged in transplantation of human organs.

Kinship

Identical twins have no problem with rejection, since they can be matched so perfectly with all the important histocompatibility leukocyte antigens. Twenty-five percent of nontwin siblings likewise show a favorable tissue match (7). Due to the way in which antigen groups are inherited within a family, they are now thought to be controlled by a series of genes at a single chromosomal locus (8).

As far back as 1967, Doctors Bernard Amos and Fritz Bach proposed that this histocompatibility locus A is the basis of a major human antigenic system whose "incompatibility strengths" are important in determining transplant acceptance. Doctor Bach, an authority in the field of immunology, has so stated it: "The likelihood of finding two unrelated individuals with the same transplantation antigens is like pushing a xylophone into a hailstorm and getting it to play "Stormy Weather" with only one mistake" (9).

The greatest problem in successful matching of people who are not related by kinship is to detect their antigens, measure the extent of their incompatibilities, and be able to predict whether the degree of incompatibility can be tolerated and the patient maintained with his transplant.

Discussion with Patient as to Risks

As previously stated, the recipient is certainly entitled to know the risks involved in the proposed surgery. Since one of the criteria for a recipient is that he must have reached the terminal stage of his illness, the main concern is not whether the knowledge of risks would cause any adverse shock to the patient, but rather, that he should be acquainted with the problem of a possible earlier death if surgery fails, or a chance at life if it succeeds.

The actual technique of surgical transplantation has been successfully accomplished and perhaps mastered. Hearts, livers, lungs and kidneys have been successfully transplanted. Surgery is risky, as all surgery is, but the technique is an accepted fact.

Problems of Rejection

The great danger is in the rejection factor. Unless the problems of rejection are conquered, the transplantation of vital organs will be increasingly limited. Following the first heart transplant, there was a surge of such operations throughout the world. On the basis of returned questionnaires, the consensus of opinion among physicians was that pressures of publicity had been responsible for the large numbers that began to be performed. This is not to say that physicians were governed by publicity, but rather, to suggest that many surgeons had the skill and knowledge necessary to attempt the surgery. When once it was begun, others began to put these skills and knowledge to work. It is to suggest, too, that the successful results of the third transplant patient, Doctor Philip Blaiberg, may have given hope to others in need of heart transplants and encouraged them to consent to such an operation. For awhile, there was a heart transplant being undertaken somewhere in the world nearly every day. However, due to the problem of rejection, a very high mortality rate has occurred — nearly 75 percent have died (10). Therefore, the number of attempts have been greatly reduced.

One surgeon, Doctor Gerd Hegemann, chief surgeon of Erlangen University Clinic in West Germany, had promised his patient, Walter Schmitthammer, that he would stop the operation if any trouble developed. He had opened the patient's chest and was preparing to insert the donor's heart when he noticed a tiny infection. "It was no bigger than a pimple," he said later. "The infection, as such, was absolutely harmless. But it could have become dangerous after the transplant, when the body is much more susceptible to infection, so I immediately decided to break off the operation" (11).

Afterward, the patient, upon learning that he still had his old heart, was disappointed at first. Then, while recovering from his infection and waiting for another chance, two other patients received heart transplants elsewhere in Germany and each died within a short time. Now, for the strange ending to the case: The patient declared, "No transplant for me!" Miraculously, his heart began to improve and he was discharged to his home. Within two months, he was well enough to return to a near-normal life. He is alive at this writing and is retired on a pension (12).

There are other indications of rejection not connected with the tissues. There are evidences of psychological rejection. These postoperative emotional problems include mood changes which may be caused by the large doses of steroids used. Psychotic reactions could be brain syndromes which may be related to rejection of the transplanted organ, or to physiological events during the surgery while the patient was on a cardiac assist device such as a pump oxygenator. If a patient becomes psychotic, the care of him becomes difficult. When drugs are administered to reduce his psychotic condition, they may also reduce his ability to describe his feelings and symptoms (13).

Use of Immunosuppressive Drugs

The human body was designed and brought into being by a masterful creator — God; and He has created a beautiful and functional piece of work. Hamlet said it well: "What a piece of work is a man! How noble in reason! How infinite in faculties! In form and moving how express and admirable! In action how like an angel! In apprehension how like a god" (14)! So wonderfully is the human body constructed that it rejects any intrusion of a foreign agent from without. Were it not for the resistance within the body toward intrusion from outside invaders, the body could not survive.

The tendency for the body to reject a transplanted organ is due to these barriers set up to protect itself from these various attacks from without. In order, then, for a foreign subject to successfully be implanted, there must be as much likeness or compatibility as possible. Tissue-typing, discussed earlier, is concerned with this, but unless organs from identical twins are used, there will be enough differences in the antigens to call for the use of immunosuppressive drugs. Rejection in renal transplants is greatly reduced when using a kidney donated from a member of a family. However, the use of kidneys from nonrelated donors can be used.

The more the antigens of a transplanted organ from a nonrelated member differ from those of the recipient, the more likely is the rejection of the organ. Drugs are used to reduce the tendency of the body to reject the foreign tissue, but these drugs will also break down the body's resistance to disease and infections and this compounds the problems of postoperative care. Often, the organ transplant is a success, but the use of so many immunosuppressive drugs to prevent rejection allows for other infections and disease to take the person in death. Physicians and biochemists are hard at work in searching for answers. Research has shown that the more compatible the tissue-matching is, the greater the success of transplantation. Some physicians feel that the ultimate success of cardiac transplantation will come in the form of an artificial heart or pump that can be safely implanted without the worry of possible rejection.

Although the use of drugs is a must in order to put down death-dealing rejection, the body is weakened considerably by them. It would seem, therefore, that the future of organ transplantation may well lie in the conquering of this rejection phenomenon by other than massive doses of drugs administered over a long span of time.

Financial Arrangements

Already, some attention has been given to the costs of human organ transplantation. It is of necessity that financial arrangements involved in transplantation of organs should be satisfactorily made before proceeding. The sympathy of the public, to which one may appeal for donations and drives, will become less easily caught as the whole area of organ transplantation catches on. While it is new and considered quite unusual, people will give that another may live. Hospitals, physicians and others can afford to write-off their fees and chalk it all up to research, publicity, or the performance of a humanitarian act of mercy. However, as the procedures grow, there will have to be a system of payment.

Grants from Government

In a study of thirty-six patients who had received cardiac transplants as of February 1, 1969, it was found that two-thirds of the total payments were provided by a combination of National Institute of Health and Hospital and/or other philanthropic sources (15). These thirty-six patients had received their heart transplants in six institutions located in the United States. At four of these institutions, no charges were made for the physicians' fees. At two other institutions, fees were charged and averaged approximately $2,400 per patient; fees for operation ranged from $1,000 to $1,500. Many of these fees were underestimated due to the fact that even in the institutions in which physicians' fees were levied, many services performed by physicians were not charged. The total charges of these thirty-six patients served by these six institutions averaged $18,694, ranging from a low of $3,300 to a high of $44,205, with five individual cases exceeding $35,000 (16).

The charges were divided as follows (17):
1. Preoperative charges: $ 2,087
2. Operative charges: $ 945
3. Postoperative charges: $15,026

There was an average charge for the donor of $636.

Payment by Patient and/or Family

The study of these thirty-six cardiac transplanted patients reveals that only four of the institutions had received any payment from the patient or family, and the largest amount paid by them was only 3.1 percent of the total charges. It should be fair to point out that while the study was in progress, patient billing was still being processed and the amount paid by the family may show an increase. It will be only a small percentage of the total charges in any case.

Courtesy Discounts by Hospital and/or Physician

In all of this, it is seen that a large amount of the expense of organ transplantation is absorbed by the courtesy discounts of physicians and hospitals. Insurance payments to physicians and hospitals have been relatively small. It is felt that some insurance companies are preparing certain types of coverage to provide for organ transplantation. These plans may include special riders at great expense, or possibly an overall rate increase to make the service available to all policyholders.

At any rate, the financial arrangements involving major organ transplantation have not been progressing with as much speed and efficiency as has that of the medical disciplines. The future of organ transplantation may, in reality, rest not upon the ability of the physician to match tissue, select donors, perform the surgery and continue treatment, nor falter because hospitals and medical centers will not provide the personnel, equipment and space in which these transplants shall be done. Rather, the future may be decided by the presence or absence of a method of meeting the financial obligations involved. Again, is this a price tag attached to human life? – or is it a sober question which must be met with as much dedication, planning and research as is involved in the medical aspects of organ transplantation?

Methods of Follow-up

To three hundred physicians, the following question was sent: "Please estimate the amount of time necessary for postoperative care of the following transplants: corneal, heart, kidney, liver."

Their answer, though varied, averaged:

Corneal: Ten days to a few weeks.
Heart: Indefinitely — years, until death.
Kidney: Three to five years.
Liver: Indefinitely.

Doctor Christiaan Barnard answered this question by stating, "Patients receiving transplants always need care." Actually, the question is ahead of the research and, at this time, there really can be no proper answer given. The majority of physicians seemed to concur by stating, "They simply did not know."

Postoperative Care

The average postoperative cost per day for the thirty-six cardiac transplant patients included in the study above was $288. These costs were varied due to the different types of care, the existing facilities, the procedures of research and the type of postoperative care given. A look at the costs of thirty kidney transplant patients cared for at Methodist Hospital, Houston, Texas, reveals a total cost of from $1,200 to $40,000, with the average cost being approximately $14,867. This average was arrived at by taking the total cost of the hospital's kidney transplant program for thirty patients ($446,011) and dividing the number of patients, thirty, into it. The total cost of their cardiac transplant program to November 1, 1969, was $274,349, or from $3,500 to $57,474 per patient (18).

Perpetual Care

As stated before, some physicians believe that the recipient of a vital organ transplant will always need care. Doctor Christiaan Barnard and others seem to feel that the physician who engages in the transplantation of human organs owes to his patients continual care. This not only may limit the number of physicians who should be engaged in transplantation of human organs, but would seem to hold those who do, to a relatively small and restricted number of patients. After all, how many patients can a physician have if he promises to each of them what amounts to perpetual care? Should this be a consideration that a physician must face before he climbs aboard the bandwagon of vital human organ transplantation? Would this not cause a physician to honestly face up to his obligations and responsibilities as he dons for himself the awesome title of "Transplant Surgeon?"

Degree of Return to Normalcy

Costs, anxieties and frustrations (mental, spiritual, and physical pain and anguish) all are a part of the program of vital human organ transplantation. Uncertainties, questionable results, length of life, and especially, the degree of return to normalcy, must be brought into the total decision as to whether or not one should have an organ transplant. These problems are not only to be faced by the proposed recipient, but must be realistically faced by members of his family. At first glance, one may feel that where the health and welfare of a loved one is concerned, none of these things matter — let us get on with it, spare no expense, limit no hardships — just spare a life and all else is secondary. This may seem quite hasty after the deed is done and one looks back over insurmountable bills; sheer physical, mental, and spiritual exhaustion, and when the constant strains brought on both the recipient and his loved ones are in evidence.

Patience wears thin, tempers shorten, tolerance weakens, and loyalty lags as the long days stretch into weeks, weeks into months. Those who were sure that transplantation of a vital organ was the only way out may find themselves now wondering if, in "cheating death," they feel they, themselves, were cheated. Perhaps not being able to verbalize these feelings, could they become deeply involved with guilt and find great difficulty in finding a mature way of expressing it? Would the love of a partner who was willing to sacrifice all, if only their loved one would live, now feel it was best for all concerned had death been welcomed? Instead of uniting the family, would it serve eventually to divide it?

Is the degree of normalcy to which a recipient of a vital human organ transplant, especially one who receives a new heart, returns, worth all that is involved? Could all this wealth, spent on such a relatively few, be better utilized to serve in building hospitals, clinics, and carry on research that could benefit, many times more, the number of patients receiving help in other more treatable areas? The total cost, based on researched and educated approximations, of caring for one hundred cardiac transplant patients who would have no guarantee of living — to say nothing of the degree of normalcy to which they may return — is $1,870,000 (19). This cost may drop as techniques become standard and procedures are stablized. Again, is it worth it? Only the patient, his involved family, and his team of medical personnel can say — and their ability to OBJECTIVELY say it may be limited, if not reversed, in light of future circumstances over which none really have control.

NOTES

1. The Holy Bible, Genesis 2:7b.
2. Consent of donor or next of kin for removal after death of tissue or organs for transplanting. Miami Heart Institute, Inc., Miami Beach, Florida.
3. Wolff, Rosemary, staff writer: Today. Cocoa, Florida, April 26, 1969.
4. Ibid.
5. Ibid.
6. Porzio, Ralph: The Transplant Age. New York, Vantage Press, 1969, p. 102.
7. Medical World News. September 6, 1968, p. 29.
8. Ibid.
9. Ibid.
10. The Miami Herald. August 17, 1969, p. 24A. The Associated Press. Used by permission.
11. National Enquirer, 44:4, 1969.
12. Ibid.
13. Cardiac Replacement. A report by Ad Hoc Task Force on Cardiac Replacement, National Heart Institute. Washington, U.S. Government Printing Office, October, 1969, p. 47.
14. Shakespeare, William: "Hamlet." Act II, Scene II, lines 316-320. Sixteen Plays of Shakespeare. George L. Kittredge, Ed. New York, Ginn and Co., 1946, p. 989.
15. Op Cit., Cardiac Replacement. p. 53.
16. Ibid., p. 51.
17. Ibid.
18. Op. Cit., Hospitals. November 1, 1969, p. 52.
19. Op. Cit., Cardiac Replacement. p. 57.

Chapter V

MORAL AND ETHICAL CONCERNS: THE PROFESSIONALS

THE professionals for this study are identified as those in the disciplines of theology, law and medicine. The concerns of these are inevitably bound together, for of all the professions, these three are time-honored servants of humanity in the real and genuine crises of life, justice, illness, death and eternity.

If there exists no real bond between these three professions, there should — for it is believed there *is* a common bond, and that it has been strengthened as an outgrowth of the new era of major human organ transplantation. Theology, law and medicine are neither weak, nor suffering any ailment that would warrant limited exercise. So, then, the rigorous expenditure of energy exacted from all three can only result in a new awareness of, and appreciation for, one another. If the transplanting of vital human organs has done nothing else, it has united these disciplines in a new understanding and acceptance of each other. For this reason, as well as many others, one can be grateful for the efforts in this area.

THEOLOGICAL VIEWS

The clergyman is concerned with the wholeness of man. He is opposed to any views or disciplines which would divide man into parts. Thus, he is interested in working with professionals such as attorneys and physicians who combine to serve man as a whole. The theologian feels that the attorney cannot honestly state that he only cares about man from the legal standpoint. The theologian feels the physician cannot treat man as a body of organs. The theologian sees man as a *person,* not just as a soul that inhabits a body. The attorney must see to the legal needs of a *person.* The physician treats man as a *person.*

Theoretical

In considering the entire aspect of human organ transplantation, the theologian is mainly concerned with man as a being — a person. He wishes man to have his rights as a person, to be treated with respect and dignity in life and in death.

He wishes man to be free from undue pressure in the decisions he makes. The theologian embraces the disciplines of law and medicine and links arms with those who will continue to see man as a person who may be either ill or in legal difficulty. The theologian will be available to function as a member of this time-honored trinity of medicine, law and theology, and is an ally, not a foe; a constructive critic, not a voice of discord; a help, not hindrance.

Practical

The place of the theologian in the field of human organ transplantation is an intensely practical one. He is concerned with being of service to those who are personally involved — the donor, the recipient, the families of each, the physicians, the institutions wherein transplants take place. He is concerned with the counseling of all who are a part of the procedure. In a very real sense, he can talk with the next of kin about the practical phases of the procedure. He can discuss the morality and ethical aspects involved. He can serve as a catalyst, he can often gain consent for a donation of a vital human organ when no one else can, and he can do this without coercion. He will always encourage the other two disciplines as they use their skills and talents for the betterment of man and his society.

LEGAL

The place of the attorney in the area of human organ transplantation is evident from the study above of the Anatomical Gift Act. The interest of the attorney is seen in the overwhelming response of the attorneys general of these fifty United States to a questionnarie sent to them by the author. It is interesting and commendable that of 750 questionnaires sent to various professionals, the return from the attorneys general was the highest: 70 percent!

The attorney has the sometimes sticky task of straightening out legal chaos when other professionals, intent on performing their "thing," fail to utilize his services beforehand. In some cases cited before, physicians have failed to consider the legal phase before performing their medical feats. In considering the moral and ethical problems, the theologian may forget there is a legal side as well. It is absolutely essential for the proper forms to be signed and witnessed before any further steps are taken in organ transplantation. The theologian and physician will err here unless legal requirements are strictly adherred to.

National Laws Enacted

That there are legal requirements as to the licensing of physicians, institutions and other such agencies and disciplines, is evidenced and acknowledged by all. It is illegal for one to practice medicine without a proper license. It is illegal for an institution to offer treatment without careful attention to the established laws.

Legal ramifications of human organ transplants are certainly in evidence. The possibility of civil liability involving surgeons, nurses and hospitals is very real. Consider the example of a heart transplant which occurred in a Brazilian hospital. After the EEG revealed no brain activity, the surgeon opened the donor's chest. After one hour and twenty-five minutes, the heart stopped beating and the surgical teams went to work. They removed the heart and transplanted it into the chest of the recipient. After it had been sutured into place, the new heart began beating without the usual electric shock. The surgeon closed the patient's chest.

Following the transplant, the common-law wife of the donor showed up at the hospital and, upon learning of the procedure threatened to sue the surgeon for removing the donor's heart without her permission. At the time of this heart transplant, a bill to legalize such quick transplants was stalled in the Brazilian legislature. The cause of the delay was that problems concerning a provision for assigning mistresses' priority over parents, brothers and sisters had not been solved (1).

The law is concerned with protecting the interests of all parties involved in any given situation. It is concerned in the area of human organ transplantation. Since the transplantation of the first human heart, legal minds have been active in seeking to carefully word legislation that would adequately protect the rights of all and make clear WHAT may be done, HOW it may be done, BY WHOM it may be done, and TO WHOM it may be done.

National laws have been and will be enacted. Due to rapid transportation facilities of today, international laws will, by necessity, be enacted to protect the rights of all. The Uniform Anatomical Gift Act, or a close version of it, will probably become part of international law as it already is becoming individual state law.

State Laws Enacted

Virtually all legislation passed or pending in the various states is patterned after the Uniform Anatimocal Gift Act. Some state legislatures have written in certain laws or provisions pertaining to their own state. The act in its entirety has been reproduced already. The variations and changes of it are minor and apply to states having some internal reasons for making the changes.

There are provisions now, also, by which a resident of one state, if fatally injured in another state, may still become a donor under laws of the state in which his death occurred, even though the laws of the two states are slightly different. For instance, suppose that a resident of Pennsylvania is killed in a traffic mishap in Maryland. If Pennsylvania's state laws differ from Maryland's in that the former requires that the would-be donor carry a donation card signed by one witness instead of two as in Maryland, and the victim's card carried only the one witness, could he become a donor under the laws of Maryland? The answer is "Yes." The Maryland Act is specific in providing that if a document of gift is executed in another state and in accordance with the laws of that state pertaining to the execution of the donation card, that same card is considered valid as a document of gift within the state of Maryland, even though the same document does not conform to the requirements of Maryland's law (2).

It now would appear that there are no questions left unanswered, but there is one — a bold one indeed — which must be faced once and for all. The Uniform Anatomical Gift Act does not, and the various state acts patterned after it do not, define death. Discussed earlier and pointed out as a problem that must be uniformly dealt with, is the definition of death. The two disciplines of law and medicine must find agreement. It can no longer hold to Black's Law of Death (3), legally accepted over the years, as being "when breathing and heart beat stop." It must either take the definition to mean "loss of brain function," or include it with "the stoppage of breathing, as death."

Before, it was noted that life must be properly defined before death could be defined. Hence, theology, law, and medicine are interrelated and inseparably bound — and this, specifically through the efforts of all three in the field of human organ transplantation.

MEDICAL

It is somewhat of an oddity that law and theology have joined with medicine in the furtherance of human organ transplantation in a way that segments within medicine have not yet joined. Theology is exploring the moral and ethical implications involved in human organ transplantation and, for the most part, has found no real barriers therein. Carefully pointing to basic principles of integrity and dignity surrounding one's person and his body, theology can assure medicine it has a broad field in which it is largely free to develop. Law has tooled the machinery, cranked it up, and started it to work out the legal barriers and problems involved, to give the utmost protection to all concerned. However, the hang-ups are in medicine itself!

Divergence of Opinion Among Internists and Surgeons

Three hundred physicians throughout the United States and some foreign countries were sent questionnaires. The question was asked, "In all honesty, do you feel publicity and public pressure have caused premature attempts at major organ transplantation?" Among the eighty who answered "Yes" were such notable men as Doctor Christiaan Barnard. These same physicians were asked, "Do you anticipate a drastic slowdown in major transplants after the interest and publicity cools?" Of the seventy-seven who answered, twenty-one replied "Yes," while fifty-six said "No."

However, their side-remarks were interesting. Some said that organ transplants would slow down "because they don't work," and "the overall results are too poor," and "they are too costly," and "donors are becoming increasingly difficult to find." Some who replied "No" had equally interesting answers. Some said, "No, because of the personalities and egos of surgeons," and "No, although publicity greatly exaggerated chances of success," and "No, feel new developments will continue and require testing and hopefully will afford advances in the art," and "No, progress does not stop," and "No, because of vast amount of corollary information being gained regarding immunology and genetics," and "No, because doctors are not affected by publicity."

However, whatever else is learned here, one thing is crystal clear: There is more difference of opinion among members of the medical profession concerning vital human organ transplants than among members of the law or theology. Now, admittedly, there was no way to determine whether the physicians were surgeons, internists, general practitioners, or others. It is felt that those who answered were represented by various specialties, and that some answered "Yes" and some answered "No." One probably should expect a greater divergence of opinion among physicians than other professionals because the questions concerning human organ transplantation are directly related to the practice of medicine.

Psychiatric and Psychological Views

Though psychiatrists are also doctors of medicine, they tend to be ranked separately from the other members of the medical profession because of their specialty. The clinical psychologists are holders of the doctor of philosophy degree and yet, by virtue of their specialty, are linked more with the psychiatrists.

These two professions seem to stand more united in their feelings than do those in law, medicine or theology. It may be because, in researching the whole area of organ transplantation, the psychiatrists and psychologists have been somewhat overlooked. They may have united because of their loneliness.

These two disciplines are concerned with the emotional shock and possible psychotic trauma that may come upon the recipient and/or his family following vital organ transplants. It is known that the long wait for a possible organ transplant has stretched emotions to the breaking point. Marital discord has been a result of organ transplants. Psychotic tendencies have been diagnosed in some heart transplant recipients. Delayed grief reactions, hostility, and extreme guilt have been discovered in both the recipient and members of his families. These cases cannot be placed within the sterile confines of an isolated medical ward and treated, as can one who is undergoing a tissue rejection. They must be treated as other serious mental and emotional disorders. It requires time, long hours of psychotherapy, patience, understanding, kindness, acceptance, and even then, the results are not clearly known. The psychiatric and psychological problems will themselves challenge someone to write specifically from this standpoint, for even if theologians agree basically upon the overall morality of human organ transplantation, and if members of the legal profession enact and execute laws governing the procedures, and if the rejection phenomena is conquered and vital organ transplanting becomes acceptable therapy — if all of this occurs — who will be on hand to prepare the patients and their families for the major adjustments in their thinking, living and actions thus necessitated? The answers surely will include the professionals from the disciplines of psychiatry and psychology.

It is hoped that in the search for answers in this area, all members involved in other aspects of the problem — physicians, attorneys, theologians, will join to find the best solutions here as they have found in the areas of the legal, the medical and the theological.

NOTES

1. Pusey, John: The legal implications of heart transplants. Quoted from

Time. June 7, 1968. Reprinted by permission.
2. Ibid.
3. Black's Law Dictionary, 4th Edition. 1951.

Chapter VI

MORAL AND ETHICAL CONCERNS: THE HOSPITAL

O FTEN overlooked in the exercise of a major medical or surgical endeavor is the institution in which the treatment and care take place. Of course, the teams of physicians are extremely vital. There can be no substitute, ever, for dedicated, skilled hands and expertly trained minds. Yet, these well-trained and competent members of the healing arts can be limited by the institutions in which they serve; or they can be utilized to their highest degree of competency by the provisions made available to them by the institutions in which they serve. Hence, in order for medicine to reach its highest potential, hospitals and medical centers must provide the necessary atmosphere, environment, personnel, and equipment to see it through.

The hospital or medical center is the focal point for the whole area of human organ transplantation. Here, the donor and recipient are both housed. Here, the laboratories and trained personnel can set up and proceed with the vital tissue-typing, an absolute necessity in organ transplantation. Here is found the multiple equipment that must be on hand; the trained personnel to operate it; the accumulation of the drugs and medicines; the sterile conditions under which it must all be done; the gathering together of the various team members – the nurse, the technician, the pathologist, the radiologist, the microbiologist, the anesthesiologist, the skilled hospital chaplain, the trained and knowledgable hospital administrator, and the governing board of trustees who set the rules and stand the responsibility for each patient admitted. All this and more is the hospital and/or medical center of today, and without these institutions, regardless of the knowledge and competence of man, there could be no success at all in the field of human organ transplantation. As a matter of fact, the skill and competence of the medical profession often must await the provisions just mentioned before their skill can be meaningfully engaged. So, then, the hospital is a vital part of the entire concern of medical endeavors. Can there be moral and ethical considerations for the hospital in the area of human organ transplantation? Are there certain requirements for institutions that must be met before it can be morally acceptable and feasible for certain organ transplants to be attempted therein?

RESPONSIBILITIES OF GOVERNING BOARD

Many do not know that the governing board of a hospital is the ultimate source of liability for a patient. It is true that there is a shared liability among such persons as the physician in charge of the patient, the anesthesiologist who administers the anesthetic, the surgeon, the technicians and others. However, the absolute, final responsibility for the care of the patient rests with the board of trustees. What awesome responsibility! Many hospitals have trustees who serve in this capacity and assume this great responsibility for sheer love of humanity and service to their God without any financial remuneration whatsoever.

To provide a good hospital and to equip it to meet the demands of a highly trained medical staff is not a small order, but to become a hospital in which major human organs can be successfully transplanted is a task that challenges one's total resources.

Before a hospital should allow any member of the staff to perform major human organ transplant surgery, the board of trustees should meet and adopt some definite rules for governing themselves in such an undertaking. The question that should first be decided is, "Do we wish to permit human organ transplantation to occur in this hospital?" The next question should be, "Do we wish to restrict or limit the type of transplant surgery to be done at this institution?" A third question that must be decided is, "Have we considered the total cost of transplant surgery and postoperative care, and are we willing to pay the price in equipment, space, personnel and time necessary for the proper care of the patients who will come?"

Unless the board of trustees is willing to decide these questions in favor of the involvements of the whole transplant problem, then it should not permit any to be done. If an institution has a moral obligation to a community to provide a service, it has a moral obligation to provide the best service possible under all existing conditions. Hence, it would be more morally acceptable for a hospital to vote against the transplantation of human organs within the confines of its institution UNLESS it plans to provide all necessary equipment, personnel and financial resources necessary to do it properly.

The question was asked of physicians throughout the United States and in some foreign countries, "What do you think the administration and board of trustees of a hospital should do to help bear the responsibility for, and participation in, the success of more major organ transplants?" Their answers were interesting and quite revealing. Some included, "Stay out of the matter," "Not qualified by training or judgment," "Stand back," "Nothing." Other answers were more discerning: "Provide legal safeguards," "Wait for developments in other hospitals," "Support the physicians," "Provide financial assistance," "Offer cooperation." A few stated, "Major human organ transplantation should take place only in university medical centers."

Aside from some of the more obvious expressions of hostility, this question reveals the lack of genuine understanding between some medical staffs and some boards of trustees. Could it be possible that the obvious has been overlooked? Have all assumed that definite lines of responsibility have been drawn, and that governing boards of hospitals and their respective medical staffs thoroughly understand their relationships? Could improvement in communication between governing boards and medical staffs be realized? Is this another good by-product to come out of the area of organ transplantation?

Since the era of human organ transplantation is now a present reality, hospitals are compelled to set up procedure outlines for organ donations and transplants. One hospital has notified all members of its medical staff: "We are in the process of setting up procedure outlines for organ donations and transplants. Until such procedures have been established at Baptist Hospital, it shall be the responsibility of the attending physicians in consultation with the Administration to secure legally proper permission for potential organ transplantation" (1).

The responsibilities of the governing board should at least incorporate the ethical guidelines, listed by the American Medical Association in 1946, concerning human experimentation (2):

(1) Voluntary consent must be obtained from the person on whom the experiment is to be performed;

(2) The dangers of each experiment must have been previously investigated by animal experimentation;

(3) The experiment must be performed under proper medical protection and management.

However, these stop far short of the guidelines necessitated since human organ transplantation has become so prevalent. In 1966, the American Medical Association adopted a longer statement. Entitled "Ethical Guidelines for Clinical Investigation," it is quoted in part (3):

In clinical investigation primarily for treatment, (1) The physician must recognize that the physician-patient relationship exists and that he is expected to exercise his professional judgment and skill in the best interest of the patient; (2) Voluntary consent must be obtained from the patient, or from his legally authorized representative if the patient lacks the capacity to consent, following: disclosure that the physician intends to use an investigational drug or experimental procedure; a reasonable explanation of the nature of the drug or procedure to be used, risks to be expected, and possible therapeutic benefits; an offer to answer any inquiries concerning the drug or procedure; and a disclosure of alternative drugs or procedures that may be available.

Each of these two guidelines were adopted during a period when transplants of vital human organs were first performed. The Judicial Council of the American Medical Association commends them as still being valid. Yet, "The Council encourages discussions of the moral, ethical, legal, social, and other aspects of clinical investigation, experimentation, and organ transplantation in human beings. It commends all efforts which encourage respect for the dignity of man, and which seek to sensitize man's ethical conscience" (4).

RESPONSIBILITIES OF ADMINISTRATION

The duty of the administrator of a hospital is twofold: (1) carry out the expressions and mandates of the board of trustees and execute the provisions of the hospital's charter, and (2) act as a liason between the medical staff and the board of trustees.

The administrator of a hospital has multiple duties and responsibilities within the framework of the above. He is to secure the best possible personnel, and envision and plan for the needs for future buildings, equipment and material. He is to represent his hospital before the community at large, and before the courts as he may be called. As the institution's chief executive officer, he is to administer the affairs of his office in such a manner as to obtain the best possible care for the patients by cooperation with the medical staff and the trustees.

The administrator is an ally of the medical profession. He may draw from the staff both criticism and praise. He may share these two offsetting emotions simultaneously, but he must not be turned toward either direction. His enforcement of the rules of the institution in which he serves will make him friends and enemies. However, he must carry out the concerns of his office, realizing that his responsibility is to the board of trustees, and to them he must ultimately answer.

In the matter of human organ transplantation, it is not correct, as some have assumed, that the board of trustees and its administrator have no area of responsibility. Quite the contrary; the board, having established rules of procedure, will expect the administrator to execute them. The physicians must desist in their thinking that the area of human organ transplantation is theirs and theirs alone. They represent the instruments and methods by which transplantation can be successfully performed. The board of trustees and the administrator must set the boundaries and limits, provide the proper environment, and furnish the people and equipment necessary for the transplantation to be done.

It is a team effort which involves the board of trustees, the administration and the medical staff, and no transplantation of vital human organ should be attempted until all three of these disciplines are in agreement.

RESPONSIBILITIES OF MEDICAL STAFF

The medical staff of a hospital is composed of these following categories: Active, Associate, Courtesy, Honorary and Consulting. The officers are elected by the medical staff and approved by the board of trustees. The number of elective officers may depend upon the size and functions of the particular hospital, but in general, they consist of the following: Chief of Staff, Assistant Chief of Staff; Secretary-Treasurer; Chief of Surgery, Assistant Chief of Surgery; Chief of Internal Medicine, Assistant Chief of Internal Medicine; Chief of General Practitioners, Assistant Chief of General Practitioners; Chief of Obstetrics and Gynecology, Assistant Chief of Obstetrics and Gynecology; Chief of Pediatrics, Assistant Chief of Pediatrics; Chief of Anesthesia, Assistant Chief of Anesthesia.

These officers are responsible for the execution of the rules and regulations of the medical staff and govern all meetings of same. Of course, each physician who has taken the oath of his honored profession shall meet the rigid requirements of the board of examiners, and upon passing, shall then be licensed to practice in the particular state in which he passed his examinations. He has chosen a profession of high ethical ideals and standards. His conduct, both professionally and personally, should merit the trust placed in him by those who trained, licensed and sent him out, and by those whom he may serve in matters of life and death. He also should uphold the high standards and abide by the policies of the institutions in which he may be privileged to serve in the practice of his profession.

The Judicial Council of the American Medical Association has prepared and adopted the following statement for guidance of physicians as they seek to reach and maintain the very highest level of ethical conduct in pursuit of their practices (5):

1. In all professional relationships between a physician and his patient, the physician's primary concern must be the health of his patient. He owes the patient his primary allegiance. This concern and allegiance must be preserved in all medical procedures, including those which involve the transplantation of an organ from one person to another where both donor and recipient are patients. Care must, therefore, be taken to protect the rights of both the donor and the recipient, and no physician may assume a responsibility in organ transplantation unless the rights of both donor and recipient are equally protected.

2. A prospective organ transplant offers no justification for relaxation of the usual standards of medical care. The physician should provide his patient, who may be a prospective organ donor, with that care usually given others being treated for a similar injury or disease.

3. When a vital, single organ is to be transplanted, the death of the donor shall have been determined by at least one physician other than the recipient's physician. Death shall be determined by the clinical judgment of the physician. In making this determination, the ethical physician will use all available, currently accepted scientific tests.

4. Full discussion of the proposed procedure with the donor and the recipient or their responsible relatives or representative is mandatory. The physician should be objective in discussing the procedure, in disclosing known risks and possible hazards, and in advising of the alternative procedures available. The physicians should not encourage expectations beyond those which the circumstances justify. The physician's interest in advancing scientific knowledge must always be secondary to his primary concern for the patient.

5. Transplant procedures of body organs should be undertaken
    1) only by physicians who possess special medical knowledge and technical competence developed through special training, study, and laboratory experience and practice, and
    2) in medical institutions with facilities adequate to protect the health and well-being of the parties to the procedure.

6. Transplantation of body organs should be undertaken only after careful evaluation of the availability and effectiveness of other possible therapy.

7. Medicine recognizes that organ transplants are newsworthy and that the public is entitled to be correctly informed about them. Normally, a scientific report of the procedures should first be made to the medical profession for review and evaluation. When dramatic aspects of medical advances prevent adherence to accepted procedures, objective, factual, and discreet public reports to the communications media may be made by a properly authorized physician, but should be followed as soon as possible by full scientific reports to the profession.

RESTRICTIONS ON PROSPECTIVE RECIPIENTS

The hospital, together with the advice of the medical staff, should work out arrangements seeking to determine the limits and boundaries of organ transplantation. Restrictions must be agreed upon and enforced regarding prospective recipients. Is it morally right to promise more than one can deliver? Should large numbers of patients be led to believe their conditions can be treatable by transplantation of a vital human organ?

At this writing, only a minute percentage of persons needing a vital organ transplant will have any likelihood of receiving one. It is unthinkable that large numbers of patients, who are possible recipients, will be admitted to a hospital and allowed to just lie around awaiting a donor with matching tissue to provide them with a needed organ. Literature in the field of organ transplantation has brought to light the fact that in some hospitals, a relatively large number of patients are classed as possible recipients.

Think of the moral entanglements here. There are vitally needed beds being occupied by some who, but for hopes of an organ transplant, would not be there. There are strains and hardships almost beyond description upon the recipient and his family as they move to a medical center, often far removed from one's home, where they hope for a transplant to give a second chance at life. One potential kidney recipient reportedly waited four and a half months for the telephone to ring with the news of a donor. During this time, the telephone was never left unguarded. Could not a hospital admit the potential recipient, do all the diagnostic tests, tissue typing, blood tests, x-rays and the like, and then dismiss the patient to his home pending the receipt of a possible donor? Also, with modern transportation making one only hours away from any destination, could not the recipient return to his own home to await his chance? Should not certain rules and regulations be adopted and executed to ease the burden of anxiety and uncertainty currently experienced by many potential recipients?

Screening, which includes not only biological and chemical, but also social, psychological and theological, is essential and should be dealt with by the hospital and medical staff as they establish other criteria for the recipient. False hope offered is worse than no hope at all. Perhaps some day, a series of centers may spring up across the countries which will serve as waiting stations for those who seek a major organ transplant. Such centers could be on the general order of a nursing home or extended-care facility.

Perhaps all the laboratory procedures — blood typing, tissue typing, x-ray and other diagnostic tests — could be made at a nearby transplant center and the potential recipient could stay at this Transplant Readiness Center (TRC) under minimum frustration and stress to himself and his family until he had the opportunity to receive his new organ. The use of skilled psychologists, psychiatrists, theologians, social workers and others could be utilized to allay undue anxiety and keep the patient in an emotional state of readiness, as he is kept in a physical state of readiness. Programs, seminars, lectures and other group teaching aides may be employed to keep the potential recipient and his family in touch with others who are in like circumstance and thus cause them to feel less alone. It may be that herein lies a major problem to be successfully solved, that of the care of the potential recipient while he awaits a transplant of a vital human organ. It certainly offers a thrilling challenge.

REQUIREMENTS INVOLVING DONORS

There are two major concerns or requirements involving donors of vital human organs.

The first is that the donor is given the same or equal care as one with the same affliction who may not be considered a donor. The fact that he may have a card or document on his person, stating his desire to be used as a donor at his death, should in no way imperil his chances for the possible recovery from his malady. Already, much has been said above of the ethical and moral responsibilities of the attending physicians to the potential donor. It is felt that, being true to their profession, physicians will give the donor every possible care and consideration. This, of course, need not include measures of therapy considered to be merely perpetuating a vegetable or preserving a cadaver.

The second major concern involving the donor is that he be treated with the dignity and respect due a person. Already, it has been said that the human being is more than a mere composite of usuable organs. He must not be viewed as spare parts for the living. Often a donor is the source of several organ transplants, giving corneas for one who is blind, a kidney or two to one who will either die or be attached to a machine for life, a heart to another, lungs, and spleen to another. In short, it is possible for a donor to give sight to two persons, life to three or four more. Surely, such a gift deserves, in return, the highest respect from those who would use these organs for others.

The donor should be given a proper burial or a dignified service of cremation when he has finished serving his fellowman. Those physicians and others involved, who give the donor this care and proper respect, merit the applause of the living and the dead. Those who view the person as a mere organ bank furnishing spare parts, for all their skill, would merit the condemnation of the living and a question could be morally and ethically raised: "How dedicated to the living can anyone be who has no proper respect for the dead?"

The donor's family should have the right to anonimity. They should not become the newscopy for the daily gossip columns. It is sad enough to give up loved ones in death. Burdens should not be multiplied by invading the private bereavement of the donor's family.

RESTRICTIONS AS TO TYPE
AND SERIOUSNESS OF TRANSPLANTS

Every transplant procedure is not a matter of life or death. There are skin grafts for cosmetic purposes, hair grafts for those sensitive to their lack of hair, bone grafts, transplanting of corneas for the blind, and others that are not a matter of whether the recipient may live or die as a result of the procedure. Many of these such transplants may take place in a relatively small and modestly equipped institution.

However, the transplantation of vital human organs, the outcome of which may mean life or death, should be performed only in hospitals and medical centers that are well-equipped by space, mechanical assists, trained personnel and which have the financial resources necessary to see the procedure through to a possible successful conclusion.

Therefore, it is felt that major organ transplantation should be done only in those certain institutions located strategically across the world that are big enough, well-equipped, and have the personnel to attempt them. Also, there should be no attempt to make heroes out of those certain ones who specialize in transplantation any more than one seeks for hero worship in the many other vital areas of preserving life. In short, why should the surgeon, who dedicates himself to specialized study, research and limitation of his surgery to organ transplantation, merit any more praise and notoriety than, for example, the general practitioner who treats his patients through the various illnesses that could take their lives? The true man of medicine neither seeks nor really wants this publicity. If one saves a life in the practice of his profession as a physician, what difference is it, really, whether he did so by transplanting a human heart, or by correctly diagnosing and properly treating a case of tuberculosis or removing a ruptured appendix? Unless treated properly, each of these will end in death, also.

The concern of all, in respect to the new area of human organ transplantation, should be that only those institutions properly equipped, financed, and staffed will be the scene of such surgery, and that only those who by specialized study, preparation and voluntary limitation of their skills to this area, do the actual transplantation of major human organs.

Does this make those institutions not so staffed and equipped less important to the communities they serve? Does this make other physicians not so limited to, and specialized in, this area less as a member of the healing arts? Should they feel or be seen by others as inferior? Definitely not! For the medical, legal and theological disciplines view each patient, client and parishioner as equally important as another, and the true professional will give his best always, and in the manner in which his specialty is called.

NOTES

1. Newsletter. Baptist Hospital of Miami, Inc., Miami, Florida. March, 1969. Mr. Ernest C. Nott, Jr., Administrator.
2. Ethical guidelines for organ transplantation. JAMA, 205:341-342, 1968.
3. Ibid.
4. Ibid.
5. Ibid.

Chapter VII

PAST, PRESENT AND FUTURE

SOME recommendations have previously been mentioned. However, in finalizing further recommendations and drawing definite conclusions, a look must be taken both at past and present accomplishments, and at prospects for the future.

TRANSPLANTS CONSIDERED ACCEPTABLE THERAPY

This question was asked of three hundred physicians throughout the United States and some foreign countries: "Which (transplants) are considered acceptable therapy – corneal, heart, kidney, liver?" Of the eighty-eight who answered, seventy-four indicated that the corneal and kidney transplants were considered acceptable therapy. Though the questions did not offer a chance for others to be named, some physicians returned side notes indicating that they considered skin grafts, bone grafts and other less delicate procedures as being acceptable therapy.

Of the vital human organs, the kidney offers the best risk for transplantation. As seen earlier, more than two thousand kidney transplants have been done and the results are very gratifying, indeed. The costs are still high and the number of those who need a transplant far exceed the supply. The technique of tissue-typing has been well-developed, and the number of such procedures successfully performed seems to qualify the kidney transplant as an acceptable form of treatment. Corneal transplants have been done over a long period of time and their success, together with the relatively low cost, makes this type of surgery an acceptable form of treatment.

TRANSPLANTS CONSIDERED EXPERIMENTAL

The remaining fourteen physicians who answered the question above were divided in their answers. Some stated that the heart was considered an acceptable transplant organ; others said the liver. However, when specifically asked if either — heart or liver — were considered experimental, the replies were sixty-eight to four that these two organs were both considered to be experimental.

PROSPECTS FOR THE FUTURE

On the basis of present accomplishments and the rate of survival of the immmediate past, surgical transplantation of vital human organs seems at first glance to have a bright future. However, when one considers the rapid increase in the number of heart transplants that were attempted soon after the first one on December 3, 1967, he sees that there has been a steady decline of late. Rejection has been, and still is, the major cause of concern in the transplantation of vital organs. Although much progress has been made in tissue-matching, and while the use of immunosuppressive drugs has helped, rejection still has not sufficiently been overcome so as to offer too much hope in the immediate future.

USE OF ARTIFICIAL ORGANS

Some transplant surgeons feel that the future of vital organ transplants must lie in the development of artificial organs. Research is deeply involved in this area, and if and when the artificial heart, for example, is developed, the problem of rejection will have been solved. Tissue-matching will be unnecessary and massive doses of drugs used in the past to combat rejection will be discontinued. This is important in many ways. Without the foreign human organ, there is no threat of rejection. With no threat of rejection, no massive uses of drugs are necessary. With the uses of these drugs greatly reduced, the serious side effects, such as weakened body resistance to disease, emotional and/or psychological and psychiatric problems, will be lessened.

Another important factor in favor of using artificial organs is that donors will be unnecessary. Also, if produced on a large scale, these artificial organs could become relatively inexpensive. The number of persons in need of a new heart is extremely high, while the number of those who will possibly receive one is less than 1 percent. However, if an artificial heart can be perfected, this number shall rise with amazing rapidity. Clearly, the way to go is in the direction of artificial organs.

The heart is essentially a pump. For this reason, of the vital organs, it offers the best chance at being artificially produced. In the 1940's, John H. Gibbon, Jr., did extensive research on a pump-oxygenator device. This temporary way of bypassing the heart and lungs proved to be successful in the first treatment of a human patient in 1953 (1). The use of heart-lung machines to support patients undergoing open-heart surgery was widespread in the late 1950's.

Research on the artificial heart began about ten years ago and there was much doubt then that a successful one could be made. However, today, the outlook is more favorable. The National Advisory Heart Council decided in 1963 to give high priority to the development of an artificial heart. After clarifying the needs of investigators regarding materials, driving mechanisms and control systems, it awarded nine contracts (2).

The Heart Institute received $500,000 from Congress during the fiscal year 1965 for use in development of an artificial heart. Six parallel contracts were awarded. These contracts were intended to define the problems and seek the best ways to approach them. A seventh contract was awarded to a systems analysis firm to analyze, evaluate and summarize information received from the other six contractors (3).

At the present time, the Artificial Heart Program is a branch of the National Heart Institute. There are four general and inter-related goals: (1) a totally implantable artificial heart, (2) an externally driven artificial heart, (3) temporary assist devices, and (4) emergency assist devices (4).

The only artificial heart ever to be transplanted in a patient was performed by Doctor Denton Cooley at Saint Lukes Hospital in Houston, Texas, on April 4, 1969. The patient lived a total of sixty-three hours.

Already, several different types of pumps have been developed. The problems so far have been that use of these various artificial pumps has resulted in considerable damage to the blood and kidneys. Nonimplanted pumps have been used successfully as assists to the natural heart which still functions within the chest. While these pumps serve to help the patient with a badly diseased heart over a period of acute emergency, what is really needed is an artificial heart that can be implanted within the patient's chest as a substitute for the diseased heart. This would, if perfected, substitute for the heart transplants now being taken from the donor. It would also eliminate the problem of rejection.

Unfortunately, such an artificial heart, with its own power source which could be implanted within the body, has not been developed. Furthermore, the experts in the field of artificial heart development feel that such a prospect is years away.

The following illustrations reproduced from the booklet, *Cardiac Replacement* and used with permission, will serve to show some of the various efforts in the development of artificial hearts (5).

FACILITIES FOR PRESERVING SPARE PARTS

Eye banks have been in existence for many years. The techniques involved in removing the corneas for safe keeping, until they can be transplanted in the eye of a recipient, have been mastered. Now, with vital human organ transplantation a reality, emphasis is being put on developing banks for the storage of these major organs.

Methodist Hospital in Houston, Texas, has in operation an organ preservation chamber in which heart, lungs and possibly other vital organs are being kept alive for future use as transplants. The chamber is reportedly so designed as to allow for transportation of these vital organs to any part of the world for possible transplants (6).

Another method of developing organ banks is in the idea proposed by Doctor Francis Y. Lau (7). He has suggested the establishing of a National Heart Donor Registry to list human hearts that may be available for transplantation. This would necessitate cooperation among physicians all over the country, and would prevent the backlog of patients waiting for donor hearts that often occurs in centers where such surgery is performed.

Another concept in the efforts for preserving spare parts is seen

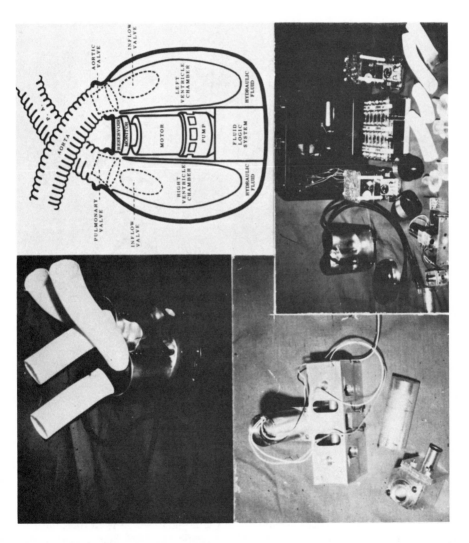

Figure 1. The Shumacker-Burns Electro-Hydraulic Heart. This device shunts hydraulic fluid from one side of the heart to the other to compress first the pulmonary and then the systemic pumping chamber. (Courtesy of National Institutes of Health.)

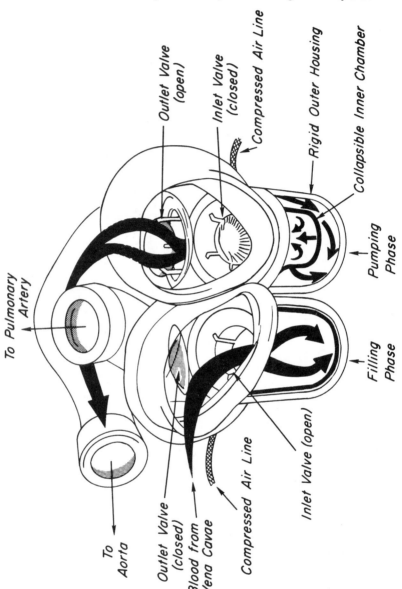

Figure 2. Kolff Total Heart Replacement. Like the normal heart, the Kolff total heart replacement is a double pump — one receiving oxygen-poor blood from the great veins and pumping it into the pulmonary artery, the other receiving oxygenated blood from the pulmonary veins and pumping it into the aorta. Although the filling and pumping phases are shown separately in the drawing, in actual operation both pumps fill together and pump together. (Courtesy of National Institutes of Health.)

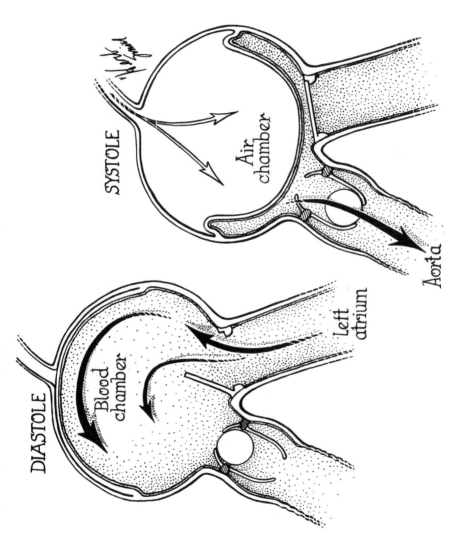

Figure 3. The DeBakey Left Ventricular Bypass Device. This pump has a collapsible blood chamber inside a rigid plastic housing. Air forced into the rigid housing collapses the blood-filled sac, propelling blood into the systemic circulation. (Courtesy of National Institutes of Health.)

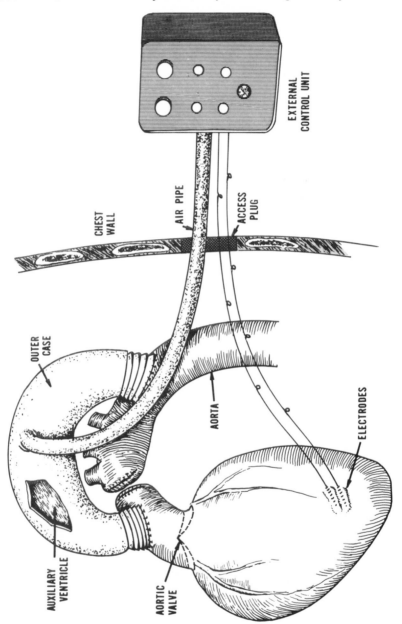

Figure 4. Kantrowitz Auxiliary Ventricle. This "booster pump" takes blood from the ascending aorta and discharges it into the descending aorta. (Courtesy of National Institutes of Health.)

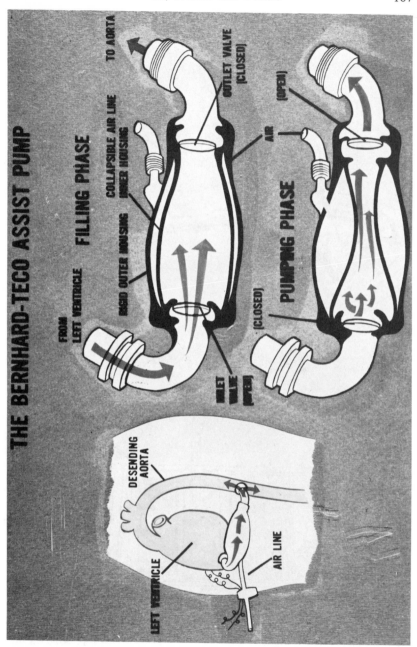

Figure 5. The Bernhard-Teco Assist Pump. In this device, blood flowing from the left ventricle during systole is passed through the outflow valve, tube, and Dacron graft to the thoracic aorta. Air pressure supplied by an external control system through a percutaneous connector is used to eject the blood that fills the bladder. (Courtesy of National Institutes of Health.)

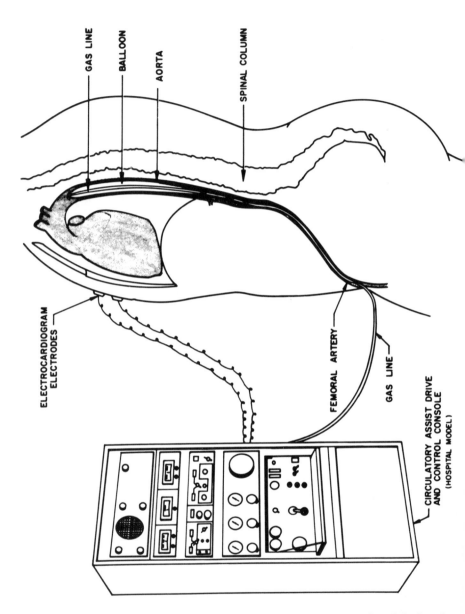

Figure 6. Kantrowitz Aortic Balloon. This circulatory assist device is inflated during the diastolic phase of the heart cycle (counter-pulsation). (Courtesy of National Institutes of Health.)

in the establishment of banks that will solicit donors who will give their organs to be used after their deaths for transplant purposes. The bank will seek donors and will prepare lists of names and organs that will be available at death. These lists will include such organs as the heart, liver, kidney, lung and others that would be sent to participating hospitals in the particular area. Under this concept, the bank would be a soliciting service only as, at this time, preservation of vital human organs has not been perfected. When death of the donor occurred, the body would be sent to a hospital, those awaiting certain types of transplants would be notified, and the transplant teams could go into action as soon as preparations could be made.

It seems that establishment of these organ banks and registries are necessary if vital organ transplants are to be carried on in any large-scale manner. Until artificial organs can be developed and made available, this will be the only means of supply. However, does this change anything? Do persons become walking organ banks with possible recipients just waiting for death to provide them with a chance to live?

The MEDICAL WORLD NEWS has suggested that the term given by garage mechanics to the practice of removing parts from old automobiles may be used in describing the practice of transplanting vital human organs in other people. They call the practice "cannibalizing" (8). If the term is disturbing, perhaps it could become less so if the emphasis is placed, as it ought to be, on the voluntary surrendering of one's vital organs at his death to be used to offer life to another. This practice may be called "brotherly love."

NEEDED THEOLOGICAL ADJUSTMENTS IN LIGHT OF THE TRANSPLANT AGE

Theologians have been challenged and their minds stretched as a result of the transplant age. Attorneys have been motivated to write new laws governing the legal aspects. Physicians have been urged on by success in lesser areas of research, and by medical and surgical accomplishments. The age of space has seen no threat to man's theological beliefs, nor will it threaten even if life should be discovered on other planets. Theology would rise to the task of representing God to those beings if they had no God, and would learn from them if they were found to have a belief in Him. Could not the same be said for theology in respect to the mysteries and marvels of vital human organ transplantation?

There is no threat to religious faith, while there are added opportunities for service to God and one's fellowman.

NOTES

1. Cardiac Replacement. A report by Ad Hoc Task Force on Cardiac Replacement, National Heart Institute. Washington, U.S. Government Printing Office, October, 1969, p. 26.
2. Ibid.
3. Ibid.
4. Ibid., p. 27.
5. Ibid., pp. 30-33. Courtesy of National Heart and Lung Institute, Bethesda, Maryland.
6. The Miami Herald. April 13-14, 1969. From Los Angeles Times, Copyright, 1969. Reprinted by permission.
7. A.M.A. News. Chicago, Illinois. Francis Y. Lau, M.D., Chief of the Cardiovascular Laboratories at Los Angeles County.
8. Medical World News. New York, March 14, 1969.

Chapter VIII

SUMMARY, RECOMMENDATIONS
AND CONCLUSIONS

W HAT shall be said about vital organ transplantation? Much. What shall be done? Hopefully, the various interested parties shall spend as much time in analyzing their thoughts and feelings about them as the physicians have in preparing to perform them. The various moral, ethical and legal guidelines discussed at length in this book should serve to aid the whole cause of vital human organ transplantation. It is *not* meant as an attempt to rule against them as a means of treating the ill.

There are some moral and ethical principles that should be employed to serve the best interests of all concerned. A brief review follows.

LIFE

Differentiation must be made between identifying life as creative and participating, and that of vegetating or artificial perpetuation. If life can be sustained by use of a vital human organ transplant that will enable one to be a creative participant and not merely a sickly onlooker, then theology can see the wisdom and the spiritual value therein. But if life is to be sustained as an increasing burden, both to the recipient and his family, or if he is spared from death to live a life that is hopelessly plagued by mounting debts, then one would question the advisibility of this second life. Again, in addition to the mere fact that a potential recipient may have matching tissue with a donor, there should be other criteria to determine whether or not he should seriously be considered for transplantation. His age may be a factor. His usefulness to society should be considered. His mental and emotional stability should be such as to warrant this second life.

How can these decisions be reached? By whose authority is one selected and others turned away? As suggested before, there should first be the involved tissue-typing to determine if the person is a potential recipient. Second, a committee consisting of physicians, psychiatrists, theologians, attorneys and possibly others could be formed to weigh these many other circumstances before a firm decision is made.

These decisions need not be made on the basis of each particular transplant to be done. A criteria could be drawn up and passed by such a committee and adopted by various states as a generally agreed-upon set of rules to govern the selection of a transplant recipient. Patterned somewhat after the Uniform Anatomical Gift Act, these criteria could be adopted by a national committee functioning similarly to the National Conference of Commissioners on Uniform State Laws, and who, having agreed upon the various parts of the whole transplant procedure, could strongly suggest these as a guideline for each possible recipient. This would seem to deal with such possible involvements as black markets, subsidies making the transplant procedure in reach of the poor as well as the rich, the manner of choice when several recipients qualify as to the tissue-matching, and the possible return of those who best may serve in, and contribute to, society. This is an awesome responsibility, and one that should be shared by the best minds among us.

DEATH

Diagnosis of death has been seen to involve both medical and legal terminology. The definition established and applied over the years may be used by the attending physician without consultation with another, and by use of the least most intricate mechanical aides – the stethoscope. But when a vital human organ is to be removed for the purpose of transplantation into another person, the more formal definition of death shall be used in addition to the consultation of at least one other physician and the aid of the EEG showing a flat reading for two hours. The attending physicians and/or those who make the pronouncement of death shall not be immediately involved with the recipient, or with the procedures of transplantation involving the organ.

Whether or not a transplantation of a vital human organ is to be performed, there is no moral or ethical reason for the sustaining of the semblance of life by artificial means when such is merely the perpetuating of a lifeless corpse.

Death is not to be considered as always an unwelcomed enemy. When the avoidance of death becomes merely an obsession or a preoccupation that interferes with the ability of one to enter into life creatively and meaningfully, it may be accepted as a reality, the ultimate destination to which all who are living are steadily moving.

Yet, the attorney, the theologian, and the physician all know that it is both illegal, immoral and ethically unsound to practice euthanasia. There must be no attempt to induce death. Nothing must be done to hasten death, even though no law, either of God or man, makes it mandatory to use unreasonable efforts to forestall it. The means cannot justify the end. One life may not be taken in order to save another. One need not, however, deny the presence of death. While simulating life by extraordinary artificial means, another may die that may possibly be spared by the transplantation of a vital human organ.

THE DONOR

The donor should be given every care and consideration that would ordinarily be given to any other patient suffering the same illness. He should be treated with dignity and respect. When death has come and his usable organs have been transplanted, his body should be given a decent burial or a dignified cremation in keeping with his own religious wishes or that of his family.

The donor should have the privilege to remain anonymous, should he so desire. He should have donated his body, or parts thereof, willingly and without coercion. Unless the deceased had refused, his next of kin may donate his body for him. Should he have attempted to sell his body or parts thereof as a benefit for his family, the offer should be duly rejected and refused. Should he have voluntarily willed that his body or parts thereof be given to research or for possible use as transplants, his next of kin should honor his request in fact, as well as by law. The donor should have the counsel of his spiritual adviser who will not put pressure on him, either to give, or not to give his body or parts for such medical use. The spiritual adviser should offer pastoral care and support in whatever decision the potential donor may choose.

The physician attending the death of a prospective donor should use all available equipment and gain the consultation of one or more physicians before pronouncement of death. These physicians shall not be a part of the team involved in the transplantation of the donor's organs.

THE RECIPIENT

The recipient shall have been duly informed of his precarious position in life and must be then in the last stages of his terminal illness. He should be duly informed of his chances of recovery should he consent to a transplant, and also be informed of the possibilities of his earlier death should a transplant be attempted. He should be told of the need for prolonged postoperative care, its cost and questionable results over a long period of time. Consent for the transplant should be obtained of the recipient's own free will and without coercion. The costs involved and the possible methods of payment should be discussed and thoroughly understood. Should he desire to cancel his consent for a transplanted organ, or should he request his physician to desist should his chances at success be unusually and suddenly lessened, his wishes should be honored while his dignity and freedom of will remain untainted.

The recipient should have access to spiritual counsel and pastoral care, and be allowed the opportunities to prepare for his own possible death. The recipient should be given the chance to work through any guilt or ambivalent feelings which may accompany his desire for a transplant. His family should be so informed that thorough understanding and open communication can take place between the recipient and the family.

If the recipient must be placed on a waiting list or standby basis, every attempt should be made to maintain as normal a life as possible and within his own familiar surroundings if feasible. The strains and anxieties engulfing the recipient and his family should be allowed to express an out, through confession, catharsis or ventilation. Any symptoms indicating emotional or psychic change of any marked degree should be promptly referred to a competent clergyman, psychologist or psychiatrist.

The consent by the recipient for a vital organ transplant should include his willingness to continue under the care and medical direction of his physician for as long as the physician deems it necessary.

THE PROFESSIONALS

The three disciplines — medicine, law and theology — are vitally related and interrelated with each other. They have been tied together by stronger bonds as a result of the transplantation of vital human organs. They have moral and ethical responsibilities, each to the other. Theology has traditionally stood by the side of both medicine and law, giving support and counsel to each. Theology applauds the efforts of both and considers their work to be one of the highest of callings as they deal with people during their times of crises in life. Theology does not bid for a place; rather, it assumes its place among these to serve the vital area of human needs untouched by either. While refusing to perpetuate an untruth, the theologian may stand with the attorney and the physician in withholding damaging truth. He will not violate the trust placed in him by either discipline, but insists upon the right to minister to the spiritual needs of those committed to his care, with or without the approval of these other two.

The attorneys have given evidence of their interest in and dedication to the new era of vital human organ transplantation by wording the laws and preparing the legislation necessary to safeguard the donor, the recipient, their families, the physicians and the institutions in which these procedures take place. He has performed his tasks well. Legislation has been passed that opens the door to virtually all forms of human organ transplants. In their preparedness, the legal minds often are ahead of either the theologians or the physicians.

The physicians have some divergence of opinion that may either help or hinder the field of organ transplantation. It could help in maintaining the high degree of preparation, research and skill essential for the success hoped for. It could hinder, if the divergent opinions cause unusual uneasiness, among the population at large. It could help, if insistence is maintained that major organ transplants be done only by physicians specially qualified by study, research and experience, and that these transplants take place at the hospitals or medical centers properly equipped, staffed, financed and with the necessary personnel and ample space to justify such procedures. It could hinder if under pressure, public or administrative, premature attempts are made to transplant vital human organs as a show of professional competence.

THE HOSPITAL

The hospital or medical center is in a period of rapid growth, and now has been recognized as within the top five industries in the United States. New medicines and drugs are being placed on the market almost daily, new treatments and therapy are becoming acceptable practice, and surgical techniques are being mastered that now includes successful transplantation of vital human organs. The hospital has a most promising future. It has a most responsible future as well.

There is a growing demand among the physicians and the patients they serve for more beds, newer equipment, more highly trained personnel and more versatility in services offered. Hospitals, and their administrators and governing boards, are being put to the test to provide the best patient care in the best equipped environs for the least possible cost to the most possible number of patients.

There can be no stopping place at some comfortable level, leaving better care to another. Hospitals have clearly been caught up in the marvels of modern medicine. The future is unlimited, but decided direction is a need to be dealt with. Hospitals, then, should decide whether to engage in major human organ transplantation or not. The decision to participate must carry with it the decision to finance the necessary space, equipment and personnel in order to offer the best possible care of the patient before and after his transplant.

As previously mentioned, this should include clear-cut procedural lines and details that the governing board, administrator and medical staff agree are essential before actual transplantation of organs begin. If the particular hospital feels transplants involve responsibilities too demanding, then the services of that institution should be so limited as to omit the procedures.

It would seem that only in the larger hospitals and/or medical centers could there be the adequate personnel, equipment, space and funding necessary for the performing of major human organ transplants.

EPILOGUE

WHILE to some the whole area of human organ transplantation seems to have opened new avenues of treatment for the terminally ill, to others it poses serious questions of risk both to the donor and to the recipient. Many notable physicians and surgeons have expressed serious disagreement as to the wisdom of entering into such extensive and experimental therapy. Among these distinguished men of medicine is Doctor Dwight E. Harken, Emeritus Clinical Professor of Surgery of the Harvard Medical School and of the Department of Surgery at Peter Bent Brigham Hospital of Boston.

Doctor Harken has taken the position that "heart transplantation in an early experimental prototype form is here." But he adds, "each man who contemplates entry into the field of cardiac transplants must arrive at his own decision by balancing the use of the considerable resources for a few transplants against his obligation to treat ailing people and extend heart surgery technics in other ways. So far, I have elected to rehabilitate a fair number of people while attempting to improve prosthetic valves, coronary circulation and mechanically assisted circulation."*

Since the early rush to perform heart transplants has now subsided, a more serious look in retrospect seems to have turned the world around to Doctor Harken's point of view. His position was stated clearly when he said, "I reserve the right to change tomorrow, but today I am proud of our restraint in not performing heart transplantations yesterday."†

One must applaud both his convictions and his open-mindedness. The whole area of human organ transplantation will profit from such words of caution.

---

*Harken, Dwight E.: Heart transplantation – A Boston perspective. *Amer J Cardiol,* 1968, p. 451.
†*Ibid.*

BIBLIOGRAPHY

BOOKS

Bowers, Margaretta K.; Jackson, Edgar N., *et al.:* Counseling the Dying. New York, Thomas Nelson & Sons, 1964.

Black's Law Dictionary, 4th ed. St. Paul, Minn., West, 1951.

Cunningham, B.J.: The Morality of Organic Transplantation. Catholic University of America Studies in Sacred Theology No. 86. Washington, D.C., The Catholic University of America Press, 1944.

Flower, Sydney, B.: The Goat-Gland Transplantation. Chicago, New Thought Books, 1921.

Jackson, Edgar N.: Understanding Grief. Nashville, Abingdon Press, 1957.

MCC. Gatch, Milton: Death: Meaning and Mortality in Christian Thought and Contemporary Culture. New York, Seabury Press, 1969.

Moore, Francis D.: Give and Take: The Development of Tissue Transplantation. Philadelphia, Saunders, 1964.

O'Donnell, T.J.: Morals in Medicine. Westminister, Md., Newman Press, 1959.

Porzio, Ralph: The Transplant Age: Reflections on the Legal and Moral Aspects of Organ Transplants. New York, Vantage Press, 1969.

Scherzer, Carl J.: Ministering to the Dying. Englewood Cliffs, Prentice-Hall, 1963.

Schmeck, Harold M.: The Semi-Artificial Man. New York, Walker, 1965.

Shakespeare, William: "Hamlet." Act II, Scene II, lines 316-320. Sixteen Plays of Shakespeare. George L. Kittredge, Ed. New York, Ginn and Co., 1946, p. 989.

Shartel, B., and Plant, M.D.: The Law of Medical Practice. Springfield, Thomas, 1959.

The Holy Bible. KJV.

The Holy Bible. RSV.

Warshofsky, Fred: The Rebuilt Man. New York, Crowell, 1965.

Webster, Noah: Unabridged Dictionary, 2nd ed. New York, Publisher's Guild, 1955.

Wolstenholme, G.E.W., and O'Connor, M., Eds.: Ethics in Medical Progress: With Special Reference to Transplantation. A Ciba Foundation Symposium. Boston, Little, Brown, 1966.

PERIODICALS

Death

Angrist, A.A.: A pathologist's experience with attitudes toward death. Rhode

121

Island Medical Journal, 43:693-697, 1960.
Ayd, F.J.: When is a person dead? Medical Science, 18:33-36, 1967.
Bard, B., and Fletcher, J.: The right to die. The Atlantic, pp. 59-64, April 1968.
Browne, I.W., and Hackett, T.P.: Emotional reactions to the threat of impending death. A study of patients on the monitor cardiac pacemaker. Irish Journal of Medical Science, 6(496):177-187, 1967.
E.D.R.S., and G.L.B.T. The moment of death: Re Potter. Medico-Legal Journal, 31(4):195-196, 1963.
Fletcher, J.: The patient's right to die. Harper's, 221:139-143, 1960. Also in Sanders, Marion K., Ed.: The Crisis in American Medicine. New York, Harper, 1961, pp. 128-137.
Gould, Donald: When is death? New Statesman, 71:841-842, 1966.
Hamlin, H.: Life or death by EEG. Journal of the American Medical Association, 190(2):112-114, 1964.

Ethical Aspects of Transplanting
Human Tissue

DeBakey, M.E.: Human cardiac transplantation. Journal of Thoracic and Cardiovascular Surgery, 55(3):447-451, 1968.
Dempster, W.J.; Melrose, D.G.; and Bentall, H.H.: Scientific, technical, and ethical considerations in cardiac transplantation. British Medical Journal, 1(5585):177-178, 1968.
Elkinton, J.R.: Moral problems in the use of borrowed organs, artificial and transplanted. Annals of Internal Medicine, 60:309-313, 1964.
Ethics in medical progress. The Medical Journal of Australia, 2(1):31-33, 1967.
Fitts, W.T., Jr., and Orloff, M.J.: Blood transfusion and Jehovah's Witnesses. Surgery, Gynecology, and Obstetrics, 108(4):502-507, 1959.
Hardy, J.D.; Chavez, C.M.; Kurrus, F.D.; Neeley, W.A.; Eraslan, S.; Turner, M.D.; Fabian, L.W.; and Labecki, T.D.: Heart transplantation in man. Developmental studies and report of a case. Journal of the American Medical Association, 188(13):1132-1140, 1964.
Harken, Dwight E.: Heart transplantation – a Boston perspective. Amererican Journal of Cardiology, 22:449-451, October, 1968. Reprinted by The Yorke Medical Group, New York, Reuben H. Donnelley Corporation, 1968.
Harken, Dwight E.: One surgeon looks at human heart transplantation. Diseases of the Chest, vol. 54, no. 4, October, 1968. Reprinted by American College of Chest Physicians.
Have a heart. Journal of the American Medical Association, 203(5):356-357, 1968.
Kass, Leon R.: A caveat on transplants. The Washington Post, January 14, 1968.

Leake, C.D.: A triumph of organ-grafting technique and its moral problems. Minnesota Medicine, 48:197-203, 1965.

Leake, C.D.: Technical triumph and moral muddle. In Starzl, T.E., Ed.: Experience in Renal Transplantation. Philadelphia, Saunders, 1964, pp. 363-370.

Ethical and Moral Issues in
Artificial Survival

Children's Hospital, and Thermo Electron Engineering Corporation: Nontechnical problem areas. Artificial Heart Program. Task II. Characterization of Biomedical and Technological Problems, Volume 2. Report No. TE 36-66, Children's Hospital Medical Center, Boston, Massachusetts, and Thermo Electron Engineering Corporation, Waltham, Massachusetts, December 1965.

Elkinton, J.R.: Life and death and the physician. Annals of Internal Medicine, 67(3):669, 1967.

Elkinton, J.R.: Medicine and the quality of life. Annals of Internal Medicine, 64(3):711-714, 1966.

General Dynamics, Convair Division: Religious, ethical, moral, legal, and economic problems. Studies Basic to Consideration of Artificial Heart Research and Development Program. Task II: Characterization of Biomedical and Technological Problems. (Prepared for the National Heart Institute.) GD/CDBD-65-044, Convair Division of General Dynamics, San Diego, October 1, 1965.

Kelly, G.: The duty of using artificial means to preserve life. Theological Studies, 11(2):203-220, 1950.

Kelly, G.: The duty to preserve life. Theological Studies, 12(4):550-556, 1951.

Lawson, H.G.: Medical irony: kidney machines saved "doomed" patients lives but raise ethical issue. Wall Street Journal, August 22, 1963.

Lister, J.:Medicine, morals, and money. New England Journal of Medicine, 276(17):971-972, 1967.

Long, P.H.: On the quantity and quality of life: II. Moral, religious, national and legal responsibilities in the care of the incurably ill or the dying. Resident Physician, 6(5):53-61, 1960.

Long, P.H.: On the quantity and quality of life: III. A discussion of the prolongation of life in the incurably ill and dying. Resident Physician, 6(6):51-53, 1960.

Nabarro, J.D.: Selection of patients for haemodialysis. Who best to make the choice? British Medical Journal, 1(5540):622, 1967.

Page, I.H.: Death with dignity. Modern Medicine, 30(21):81-82, 1962.

Scribner, B.H.: Ethical problems of using artificial organs to sustain human life. (Presidential address) Transactions of the American Society for Artificial Internal Organs, 10:209-212, 1964.

Transplantation Proceedings, 1(1):Part I, 1969; 1(1):Part II, 1969; 1(2):1969; 1(3):1969.

General

Archdiocese of Miami: Notes on moral theology. Theological Studies, 29(4):1968.

Collins, Reverend Raymond: Heart transplants ethical considerations. Catholic Lawyer. Winter, 1969.

Crane, Diana: Social Aspects of the Prolongation of Life. Russell Sage Foundation, 1969.

Ford, Thomas J.: Human organ transplantation: legal aspects. Catholic Lawyer, Spring, 1969.

Heustis, Albert E.: The two gates of life. Dilemmas in Faith and the Scientific Manipulation of Life and Death. Council for Health and Welfare Services, United Church Board for Homeland Ministries, United Church of Christ. Lee W. Rockwell, general secretary.

Irion, Paul E.: That life shall have meaning. Dilemmas in Faith and the Scientific Manipulation of Life and Death. United Church of Christ. Lee W. Rockwell, general secretary.

National Heart Institute: Cardiac Replacement. Ad Hoc Task Force report. Washington, U.S. Government Printing Office, October, 1969.

Schoenberg, Bernard, Ed.: The right to die in dignity; The definition of death; Death. Archives of the Foundation of Thanatology. Foundation of Thanatology. New York, 1969.

The American College of Cardiology. Fifth Bethesda Conference of the American College of Cardiology, Bethesda, Maryland, September 28-29, 1968.

Wright, Carroll J., *et al.:* The Faith of Your Patients: A Handbook on Religious Attitudes Toward Medical Practices. Los Angeles County Medical Association, 1969.

Legal Aspects of Transplanting Human Tissue

After you've gone. Journal of the American Medical Association, 175(2):135, 1961.

Black, Herbert: Doctors appeal for organs for transplant surgery. The Boston Globe, Boston, February 4, 1968.

Commissioners on uniform state laws. Uniform Anatomical Gift Act. National Conference of Commissioners on Uniform State Laws, Philadelphia, July, 1968.

Curran, W.J.: A problem of consent: kidney transplantation in minors. New York University Law Review, 34:891-898, 1959.

Dilemma of irreversible renal failure. British Medical Journal, 1(5540):581-582, 1967.

Ford, J.C.: Refusal of blood transfusions by Jehovah's Witnesses. Catholic Lawyer, 10(3):212-226, 1964.

Grahm, Fred P.: Who owns the body? The New York Times, January 7, 1968, p. E9.

Hershey, Nathan: Obtaining consent for the use of body tissue. American Journal of Nursing, 63(8):105-106, 1963.

Packel, I.: Spare parts for the human engine. Pennsylvania Bar Association Quarterly, 37(1):71-77, 1965.

Shapiro, H.A.: Organ grafting in man. Journal of Forensic Medicine, 14(2):41-45, 1967.

The transplant issues: ethical, legal, and scientific. Richmond Times-Dispatch, Richmond, Virginia, January 28, 1968.

Thurston, G.: Problems of consent. British Medical Journal, 1(5500):1405-1407, 1966.

Wasmuth, C.E.: Legal aspects of organ transplantation. Anesthesia and Analgesia Current Researches, 46(1):25-27, 1967.

Wasmuth, C.E., and Stewart, B.H.: Medical and legal aspects of human organ transplantation. Cleveland-Marshall Law Review, 14(3):442-471, 1965.

Williams, L.N.: Medicine and the law: renal transplantation from mortally injured man. Lancet, 2:294, 1963.

Medical Experimentation on Human Subjects

Lynch, John J.: Human experimentation in medicine: moral aspects. Part III. Symposium on the study of drugs in man. Clinical Pharmacology and Therapeutics, 1:396-400, 1960.

Psychological Issues in Artificial Survival

Abram, H.S.: The psychiatrist, the treatment of chronic renal failure, and the prolongation of life. American Journal of Psychiatry, 124(10):1351-1358, 1968.

Bend, E., and Callahan, T.E.: Artificial heart raises real hospital issues. Modern Hospital, 107:71-73, 1966.

Psychological Aspects of Transplanting Human Tissue

Colomb, Georges, and Hamburger, Jean: Psychological and moral problems of renal transplantation. In Abram, H.S., Ed.: Psychological Aspects of

Surgery. Boston, Little, Brown, 1967. International Psychiatry Clinics, 4(2):157-177, 1967.

Kemph, J.P.: Renal failure, artificial kidney and kidney transplant. American Journal of Psychiatry, 122(11):1270-1274, 1966.

Riley, C.M.: Thoughts about kidney homotransplantation in children. Journal of Pediatrics, 65(5):797-800, 1964.

Tyler, H.R.: Neurological complications of dialysis, transplantation, and other forms of treatment in chronic uremia. Neurology, 15(12):1081-1088, 1965.

Wilson, W.P., and Stickel, D.L.: Psychiatric observations of recipients and donors in renal transplant procedures. Speech presented at the Transplantation Seminar for Science Writers, sponsored by Duke University and the National Institute of Allergy and Infectious Diseases, Durham, North Carolina, February 27-28, 1967.

Reporting Medical Advances to the Public

Heart transplants: how many, how soon? Medical World News, February 16, 1968.

World's third heart transplantation. Journal of the American Medical Association, 203(5):374, 1968.

Social Issues in Artificial Survival

Borrowed time. New England Journal of Medicine, 276:1206-1207, 1967.

Eschbach, J.W.; Barnett, B.M.S.; Daly, S.; Cole, J.J.; and Schribner, B.H.: Hemodialysis in the home — a new approach to the treatment of chronic uremia. Annals of Internal Medicine, 67(6):1149-1162, 1967.

Hittman Associates: Final Summary Report on Six Studies Basic to Consideration of the Artificial Heart Program. (Prepared for the National Institutes of Health.) HIT-235, Hittman Associates, Baltimore, Md., October 24, 1966.

Nesbitt, Lynda: Nursing the patient on long-term homodialysis. Canadian Nurse, 63(10):40-41, 1967.

Page, I.H.: Prolongation of life in affluent society. Modern Medicine, pp. 89-91, October 14, 1963.

Retan, J.W., and Lewis, H.Y.: Repeated dialysis of indigent patients for chronic renal failure. Annals of Internal Medicine, 64(2):284-292, 1966.

NEWSPAPERS AND MAGAZINES

Anderson, Fred: Who will decide who is to live. New Republic. Washington, D.C., April 19, 1969.

A.M.A. News. Chicago, Illinois.

Beacon Journal. Akron, Ohio, June 1, 1969.

Maston, T.B.: Death with dignity. Florida Baptist Witness. Jacksonville, Florida. August, 1969, p. 5.

Medical Tribune, New York, April 21, 1969.

Medical World News. September 6, 1968, p. 29. March 4, 1969.

National Enquirer, 44(6):4, 1969.

Newsweek. New York, May 20, 1968.

Stevens, Leonard A.: When is death? The Reader's Digest. Pleasantville, New York, 1969, pp. 225-226.

The Miami Herald. Miami, Florida. January 29, 1969, p. 22; April 6, 1969. p. 20A; April 13-14, 1969; May 22, 1969, p. 30H; August 17, 1969, p. 24A.

The Miami News. Miami, Florida. February 8, 1969. p. 5B; March 10, 1969; September 25, 1969, pp. 9C, 8A; January 22, 1970.

Time, The Weekly Magazine. New York, June 7, 1968.

Today. Rosemary Wolff, staff writer. Cocoa, Florida. April 26, 1969.

UNPUBLISHED MATERIALS

Di Prima, Sister M. Josetta, O.S.F.: The morality of heart transplants. Unpublished master's thesis, St. Xavier College, July, 1968.

Miami Heart Institue: Consent of donor; Consent to operation for transplantation of human organs. Miami Beach, Florida.

Newsletter. Baptist Hospital of Miami, Miami, Florida. Ernest C. Nott, Jr., administrator.

Pusey, John R.: The legal implications of heart transplants. Unpublished lecture, 1969.

INDEX

A

Accident-prone person, 39
Administrators of hospitals, xiv
duty of, 91-92
American Bar Association and the Uniform Anatomical Gift Act, 49
American Electroencephalographic Society, 28
American Medical Association, human experimentation guidelines, 91
Anatomical Gift Act, 43, 49-55
and attorney, 80-81
persons who many execute, 50
Anesthetic doses and isoelectric EEG, 28
Animal experimentation, 91
Anonimity of donor, 97
Antigen groups, 71
and rejection, 74
Arterial pressure and documentation of death, 30
Artifactual activity and death, 26
Artificial heart, 74, 101
Artificial Heart Program, 101
Artificial insemination, 11, 12
and the Baptist Church, 46
and Liberal Judaism, 47
and Orthodox Judaism, 47
and the Roman Catholic Church, 47
Artificial life, 21
Artificial organs, 100
Assist devices, emergency and temporary, 101
Attorneys, 80
Attorneys general, xiv
and the Anatomical Gift Act, 50
Autopsy, 55
Autotransplantation of the uterus, 11

B

Banks, 109

Baptists, and organ transplantation, 45
Barnard, Christiaan, xxvi
Bible, xiv, xxv
and Jehovah's Witnesses, 5
and Scriptural evidence of healing, 44-45
Bills, medical, and the recipient, 68
Biological life, 19
Biomedical makeup of recipient, 70
Black market, 69, 112
Blood
analysis and irreversible coma, 28
pressure and time of death, 58
transfusions, 5
type, 71
Board of trustees, 89, 92
Body
disposition of, 43
donation of, xviii, 42
sale of, 113
transplants, 14
willing of, xxii, 48, 51-52
Bone grafts, 5
Brain
death of, 26, 58
definition, 26
and moral implications, 13
syndromes, 73
transplantation of, xix, 13-16
Breathing, 26
absence of and documentation of death, 30, 58

C

Cadaver
donor, 31
eyes, removal of and Judaism, 47
organs from, 5, 26
Cancer patients, ix
Caloric test and determination of death, 30

Cardiac transplants, (epilogue)
    see also Heart transplantation
Catharsis, 63
Central nervous system depressants and
    isoelectric EEG, 28
Certifying death, 29, 31
Chaplains, xiv, xv
Chromosomal locus, 71
Circulation
    of blood, stoppage of, 25
    mechanically assisted, (epilogue)
Civil liability, 82
Clergy, xvii
    and spiritual support for recipient, 64
Clinical death, determination of, xxii, 48
Clinical investigation, 91
Coma, 26
Confessional, 63
Consent
    by authorized representative, 64
    form, 65-67
    by next of kin, 54
    for surgery, 63
    voluntary, 114
Consent to operation for transplanting
    human organs, form, 65-67
Consultation, (foreword)
Corneal
    reflexes and documentation of death,
        30
    transplants, 5
Coronary
    care unit, xxiii
    circulation, (epilogue)
Cost, 67-69
    and cardiac transplants, 75
    hair grafts, 10
    home dialysis, 23
    and guilt feelings, 63
    kidney machine, 23
    kidney transplants, 6, 23
    liver transplants, 75
    lung transplants, 6-7
    of postoperative care, 77
Cremation, 97
Criminal actions and death of donor, 55

D

Death

brain, 26, 38
certification of, 31
clinical, determination of, xxii, 56
from criminal actions, 55, 56
definition of, xvi, 23-31, 38, 112
determination of by physician, 30, 58
documentation of, 30
and euthanasia, 31-40
and flat EEG, 29
legal, 25, 26, 27, 56
premature, 21, 29
preparation for, 62
and rejection, 71
rights and duty of, 53
and spiritual preparation, 61
statement on, 25-26
and telling the patient, 34-35
and theologians, 36
time of, 28, 53, 58
and willing of body, 48-49, 52
Decedent and the Uniform Anatomical
    Gift Act, 50
Denominational
    backgrounds, xiv
    morality and transplantation, xvi, xix
    policies concerning transplantations,
        xxi, 45-47
Dental schools and anatomical gifts, 51
Desire to live, 39
Dialysis, home, 23
Disposition of body, 53
Doctrinal barriers in transplantation,
    46-47
Document of gift, 52
Documentation of death, 30
Donate body, and the Anatomical Gift
    Act, 42, 49-55
Donation card, 83
Donees and the Anatomical Gift Act, 51
Donor, xiv
    burial of, 44, 47
    in death, 42
    death from criminal actions, 55
    and denominational policies, 44-47
    document of gift, 52
    and insurance premiums, 42
    requirements of, 96-97
    and rules regulating physicians, 57
    of a transplanted brain, 15

and the Uniform Anatomical Gift Act, 49-55
Drugs
immunosuppressive, 12
intoxication from, 26
and rejection, 74

E

Ecclesiastes, 17-18
Electroencephalograph (EEG), 22, 26
to determine death, 58
"flat," 28, 29
recording irreversible coma, 28
Embalming, 53
Embryos, laboratory-fertilized, 12
Emotional
life, definition of, 19
problems, 73
shock, 86
Episcopal Church and organ transplantation, 46
Euthanasia, 31-40, 113
positive, 36
and theological implications, 35
Experimental transplants, 99-100
Eye banks, 102

F

Family's consent, 48
Federal grants, 23, 68, 75
Fees for operation, 75
see also Cost
Fertilization of human eggs in test tubes, 12
Financial arrangements, 74
"Flat EEG's," 28
and determination of death, 29
see also Electroencephalograph
Follow-up, methods of, 76-77
Foreign countries, xiv
and the Anatomical Gift Act, 53
Funeral services, 53

G

Genes and ovary transplants, 11
Genital organs transplants, 11

Gift
amendment or revocation of, 53
document of, 52
Governing board of a hospital, 89-91
Government subsidy for organ transplantation, 68
Grafts
bone, 5
hair, 10
skin, 5
"strip," 10
Grants from government, 75
Grief reactions and heart transplants, 86
Guilt feelings, 63, 86

H

Hair grafts, 10
Healing, Scriptural evidence of, 44, 45
Heart transplantation, 7-8
artificial, 74, 101
and denominational morality, xvi
donor and pronouncement of death, 29
lung machines, 101
and psychotic tendencies, 86
Hemodialysis treatment, 22
Heredity and ovary transplants, 11
Histocompatibility locus, 71
Hospital chaplains and morality of human organ transplantation, xv
Hospitals and organ transplantation, xxiii, 88-98
cost, 68, 74-75
future of, 116
governing boards, 89-91
and insurance companies, 76
Hostility and heart transplants, 86
Human eggs, fertilization of in test tubes, 12
Human Kidney Transplant Registry, 4, 5
Human vegetable, xvi
Hypocarbia, 30
Hypothermia, 26

I

Immunosuppressive drugs, 12
and rejection, 71, 73-74

Implantable artificial heart, 101
Incompatibility strengths, 71
Incurable diseases
  and euthanasia, 32
  and selection of patients for trans-
    plantation, 70
Infections, 12
Infertile women, 12-13
Insurance companies, 42
Intellectual life, definition of, 19-20
International laws, 83
Institute of Forensic Science, 30
Intensive care unit, xxiii
Investigational drugs, 91
Isoelectric EEG's, 28
  and documentation of death, 30
  see also Electroencephalograph

J

Jehovah's Witnesses, 5
Jesus Christ, 15-16
Judaism and organ transplantation,
  46-47

K

Kidney machine, 22
Kidney transplant, ix
  cost of, 6
  and National Health Institutes, 6
  rate of success, 62
Kin, next of, 42
  and the Anatomical Gift Act, 54
  and permission for transplants, 43, 48
Kinship and organ transplantation, 71

L

Larynx transplant, 9
Last rites, 62
Last Will and Testament, 48
Laws
  international, 83
  national, 82-83
  state, 83-84
Legal implications and organ transplantation, xxi, 47-48
  and attorney, 81

consent, 64
death, 25
  time of, 26
Legislative procedures, xxii
Leukocyte antigens, 71
Life
  artificial, 21
  biological, 19
  definition of, 19
  emotional, 19
  expectancy, 21
  intellectual, 19
  organic, 19
  proneness, 39
  sanctity of, 17
  spiritual, 20
Liver transplants, 6-7
Lung transplants, 7

M

Marital discord and organ transplants, 86
Maryland Act, 83-84
Mechanical devices, 21
  to determine death, 58
Medical centers, xxiii
  and anatomical gifts, 51
Medical staff, xxiii, 88-91, 92-94
Medicinal stimulants, 21
Menopause and ovary transplantation,
  11
Mercy killing, 32
  see also Euthanasia
Ministers, xiv
Minor and consent for transplantation,
  64
Morality of human organ transplanta-
  tion, xv, xix
Mortality rate and rejection, 72
Murder, 18
Muscular movements and documentation
  of death, 30
Mutilation, act of, 47

N

National Conference of Commissioners
  on Uniform State Laws, 49
National Heart Donor Registry, 102

National Heart Institute, 5
Artificial Heart Program, 101
National Institute of Health and
Hospital, 75
National laws, 82-83
Natural life, 19
Nerve fibers in the spinal cord, 15
Normalcy, return to, 78

O

Oath of Hippocrates, 32-33
Organ banks, 109
Organ donation
and the hospital, 90
and Judaism, 47
and the physician, 94
see also Donor
Organ preservation chamber, 102
Organ transplantation, xiii
cost, 68, 74-75
and denominational policies, 45-47
history of, 3-16
and hospitals, xxiii, 88-98
and Jehovah's Witnesses, 5
and kinship, 43, 48, 54, 71
legal implications of, xxi-xxii, 47-48
literature on, xxiv-xxvi
morality of and hospital chaplains, xv
parish clergymen's views on, xix
Organic life, 19
Ovarian tissue, dangers of transplantation, 12
Ovary transplants, 11

P

Pacemaker, 21, 38
Pain, 60
Painless death, 31
see also Euthanasia
Pancreas transplant, 9
Parish clergy, xiv
and human organ transplantation, xix
questionnaires, xx
Pastoral care, 63, 114
Patients, cancer, ix
Payment, method of, 68, 74, 114
see also Cost

Permission for removal of organs, xxii
and the hospital, 91
see also Consent
Perpetual care, 77
Perpetuation, artificial, 111
Personal rights, violated, 48
Physicians, xiv
and the Anatomical Gift Act, 50
legal action against, 48
moral and ethical implications involved in transplantation, xvii-xviii
and perpetual care of patient, 77
and pronouncement of death, 25, 30
regulating rules, 57
responsibility of donor, 57
statement of guidance, 93-94
Plantar responses and documentation of death, 30
Positive euthanasia, 36
Postoperative care, 74, 77
Postural activity, 30
Premature death, 21, 29, 39
Priests, xiv
Professors and moral and ethical implications of transplantation, xviii
Prolonging life, limits, 61-62
Pronouncement of death, 25
guidelines, 30
and heart donor, 29
and physicians, 57, 58
and recipient, 112
Prosthetic valves, (epilogue)
Psychiatric
screening of recipient, 71
views of organ transplantation, 86
Psychic change, 115
Psychological
rejection, 73
views on transplantation, 85
Psychology, professors of, xiv
Psychotherapy, 86
Psychotic
reactions, 73
trauma, 86
Public Information Center, 4
Public pressure and organ transplantation, 85
Public reports of organ transplants, 94
Publicity, undue, 43

Pump oxygenator, 73, 101
Pumps, 101-102

Q

Qualifications for eligibility of recipients, 70
Questionnaires, xiv

R

Rabbis, xiv
Recipient, xiv
  confession, 63
  consent for surgery, 63
    form, 65-67
  and discussion of risks, 72
  emotional stability of, 111
  and financial arrangements, 67-69
  last rites, 62
  moral and ethical concerns, 60-79
  and preparation for death, 62
  psychiatric screening, 71
  restrictions on, 94-95
  and rules regulating physicians, 57
  selection of, 70, 112
  spiritual preparation, 61, 64
  "stand-by," 70
  tissue-typing, 71
Recovery and isoelectric EEG, 28
Reflexes and brain death, 26
Registries, organ, 109
Religion *see* Theology and specific denomination
Rejection
  and artificial organ, 100
  and death, 71
  and heart transplants, 8
  and identical twins, 71
  problems of, 72, 100
  psychological, 73
Renal transplants and rejection, 74
Requirements, legal, xxii
Research
  adequacy of, xix
  and anatomical gifts, 51
  and artificial organs, 100
  method of, xiv
Resistance to disease and artificial

organs, 100
Respirators, 38
Responsibility of physicians, 57-58
Restrictions on recipients, 94-96
Resuscitation, 26
Revocation of gift, 53
Risk, (epilogue)
  discussion of with patient, 72
  and kidney transplantation, 62
  surgical and cancer patients, ix
Roman Catholic Church and organ transplantation, 46

S

Sacrament to the dying, 63
Scalp transplants, 10
Scientific reports of organ transplants, 94
Screening of recipient, 95
Self-preservation, 60
Sell body, 113
Sex transplants, 10
  and the Roman Catholic Church, 46
Sibling, nontwin, 71
Skin grafts, 5
"Spot-sodding," 10
Soul, xvii
  and moral implications of transplantation, xix
Spare parts, facilities for preserving, 102
Spinal cord, nerve fibers in, 15
Spiritual life, definition of, 20
Spiritual preparation, 61, 63
Spleen transplant, 8-9
"Stand-by" condition of recipient, 70, 114
State laws, 83-84
Steroids, 73
Stimulants, medicinal, 21
Storage of human bodies, 50
"Strip grafts," 10
Success of transplantation and time of death, 38
  rate of, 62
Superficial reflexes and documentation of death, 30
Sustaining life, xiii
  by artificial means, xvi

Synoptic Gospels, 44

T

Tax-supported institutions, 68-69
Tendon reflexes and documentation of
   death, 30
Terminally ill patient, 21, 60
   and organ transplant, 70
Terms of gift, 53
Test tube babies, 12
Theologians
   and euthanasia, 35, 36
   and preparation for death, 62
   and terminal illness, 32, 37
   views on transplantation, 45, 80
Theology and transplantation, xix-xx,
   44-47
   Baptists, 45
   Episcopalian, 46
   Judaism, 46, 47
   Roman Catholic, 46
   professors of, xiv
Thymus transplant, 9
Time of death, 25
   and physicians responsibility, 25, 58
   pronouncement guidelines, 30
Tissue-matching, 70
Tissue-typing, 70, 71
Transfusions, blood, 5
Transplant
   acceptance, 71
   center, 96
   recipient and family, 69
   team, 58
Transplant Readiness Center (TRC), 96
Transplantation
   and Anatomical Gift Act, 43
   antigens, 71
   body, 14
   brain, 13-16
   and cadaver donor, 31
   consent of next of kin, 54
   and denominational policies, xxi,
   45-47
   and ethics, 25

   and euthanasia, 32-40
   financial arrangements, 67-69
   genital organs, 11
   and Jehovah's Witnesses, 5
   kidney, ix, 6
   larynx, 9
   liver, 6-7
   lung, 7
   pancreas, 9
   rate of success, 62
   and rejection, 72-74
   scalp, 10
   spleen, 8
   theologians views on, xix-xx
   thymus, 9
   time of death and, 26, 58
Transportation of vital organs, 102
Twins, identical and rejection, 71

U

Uniform Anatomical Gift Act, xxii, 25,
   49-55
   and state laws, 83-84
University of Colorado Medical School,
   7
University medical centers, 90
Usable organs and donor, 113
Uterus, autotransplantation of, 11

V

Valves, prosthetic, (epilogue)
Ventilation, 63
Vital signs, absence of, 25, 26
   and determination of time of death,
   58
Voluntary consent, 91

W

Waiting list, 114
Will to live, 60
Willing of one's body, xxii, 48, 51-52
   revocation of gift, 53